THE ART of JUDGE DREDD

THE MOVIE

B XTREE

First published by
Boxtree Limited,
Broadwall House,
21 Broadwall,
London SE1 9PL.

1 2 3 4 5 6 7 8 9 10

Designed by Nigel Davies, Stone Studio.

Script edited by David Chute.

Picture credits.
David Allday: pages 52 *bottom*, 53
Julian Caldow: pages 16 *top left*, 34, 35, 42 *centre right & right*, 49 *right & bottom*, 54 *top*, 65 *top & third
down*, 71 *right*, 77 *top*, 124 *top*
Danny Cannon: pages 46 *bottom*, 47 *bottom*
Matt Codd: pages 12, 80 *top*, 81, 86–87, 88–89, 90–91, 154
Robbie Consing: pages 32, 75, 150, 152–153
John Greaves: pages 56 *bottom*, 57 *bottom*, 112, 113
Chris Halls: pages 33 *top*, 62, 65 *bottom left*, 96
Martyn John: pages 16 *top right*, 33 *middle & bottom*, 136, 137
Little John: page 42 *centre left & left*
Simon Merton: page 80 *bottom*
Nigel Phelps: pages 71 *bottom*, 77 *bottom*, 130 *bottom*
Emma Porteous: page 54 *bottom*
Kevin Walker: pages 57 *top*, 63, 71 *centre left*, 124 *bottom*
David Woodhouse: page 65 *second down*
All other pictures as credited in the captions

While every effort has been made to credit the work in this book correctly, the publisher apologises for any
regrettable omissions at the time of going to press.

Printed and bound in UK by Cambus Litho Ltd.

ISBN: 07522 0666 4

THE ART OF JUDGE DREDD

THE MOVIE

Includes the complete shooting script of the film by
WILLIAM WISHER and STEVEN E. DE SOUZA
and the production art by
NIGEL PHELPS
and his team

    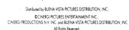

TYPICAL CROSS SECTION

MEGA CITY ONE

INTRODUCTION

Screenplays are where a movie starts. Before an actor says a single word. Before a director takes his first step onto a set. Before a frame of film is loaded into the camera. There is a guy sitting alone in a room somewhere staring at a blank sheet of paper and listening to the clock tick. That person is the first one to make the movie. Every time another person comes into the process the movie gets made again. And it changes a little more each time. Like the game we played as children when you sit in a circle and whisper a word into the ear of the person next to you and they whisper it to the person next to them and so on. And at the end of the circle the word comes back to you and it's never the one you started with. Movies are like that. They grow. And they change. They become the sum of everyone who worked on them.

I like writing them. Because none of that has happened yet. I'm the first one who ever gets to see it. And it's exactly the way I want it to be. I laugh at all the jokes. I worry when the good guy is in trouble. And I fall in love like he does with the girl.

It's a funny way to make a living. Because essentially, you're getting paid to watch a movie inside your head, and write it down. After that, it's not really yours anymore. Sometimes it's better. It's almost always shorter. And once in a while the actors say things you never heard before.

This movie started for me over lunch in November of 1991. Cottie Chubb wanted to talk to me about the English comic book that Pressman Films hoped to bring to the screen. Cottie and I got to know each other a few years before when a location scout with a dark sense of humour had us inching a six-foot-wide Plymouth Voyager down a five-foot-wide track along a sheer cliff face in the mountains of Utah. Neither of us was laughing but we didn't die either so we had to become friends. I've always trusted him.

I remember looking at the comic book for the first time. The artwork was wonderful. Dark. Intense. The humour was edgy enough to cut glass with. Dredd. Cop. Judge. Jury. And often, executioner. An unforgiving hero in a violent and frightening future. It was great. It was funny. It was powerful. I was hooked. But it was scary too. Because I mean let's face it the guy's a fascist. In any normal story he'd be the villain. It worked just fine in the comic. But to translate Dredd's world to the screen would take a big budget. And a big budget would require a big audience. And I wasn't sure how to keep Dredd who he was and make him someone I could really care about. And if I couldn't care about him, how could I hope to convince anyone else to?

The other thing we had to deal with was the story. Specifically, what was it going to be? The comic was a series of short episodes. All of them filled with wild characters and pungent black comedy. But none of them written to support three acts. There was going to be work to do.

I spent the next few months thinking about it while I was completing other commitments. But finally we were able to sit down to do it. Cottie and Ed Pressman and Charley Lippincott and Susan Nicoletti. The gang of four. My co-conspirators. We kicked around many ideas in those first few weeks. We passed around comic books. We all went back to the images time and again. That one which stayed always like a fixed point around which everything whirled was Judge Dredd, feet planted firmly, the Book of the Law in one hand, the Lawgiver in the other. The embodiment of harsh justice. That was the center of the movie. Everything would flow from there.

They were patient and generous. They listened. They gave good advice. They let me smoke cigarettes. And, ultimately, they gave me room to work it out. The solutions came out of the story of Dredd and Rico. Dredd's dark mirror in flesh and blood. The reflection of Dredd twisted onto hate. Of himself gone wrong. And out of that came Dredd's capacity for self-doubt. And resurrection. And finally, humanity.

So I went home to write down the movie I saw in my head. I liked this one a lot. It had taken a year to negotiate the track between that first lunch and the finalized first draft. But the movie was going forward. The green light had been given. And it wasn't just mine anymore. It was real now.

Andy Vajna stepped up to make it happen; Cinergi would write the cheques to give it life. Sylvester Stallone would add flesh to the image of Judge Dredd we'd held in our heads. And Nigel Phelps would begin to show us what Dredd's world was going to look like.

I remember the excitement I felt the first time I saw the artwork that he and his team were creating. The movie was growing. It was coming to life before my eyes. Mega-City and the Cursed Earth weren't just sketches in a comic book, or images in my imagination. They were turning into real places. Vivid. Frightening. Spectacular places we can all go to in a theater in the dark.

I hope you like his vision as much as I do. It's his movie too now. And I feel very lucky for it. Thanks, Nigel.

William Wisher, Los Angeles, 1995

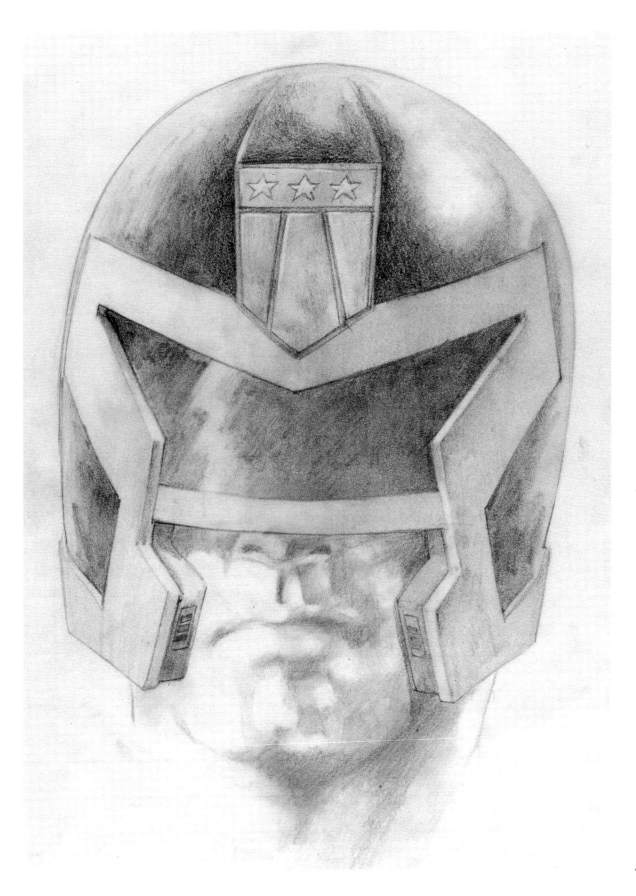

Drawing by Simon Murton.

THE SCREEN IS BLACK

A VOICE: "In the Third Millennium, the world changed. Climate. Nations. All were in upheaval. Humanity itself turned as violent as the planet. Civilization threatened to collapse. And then . . . a solution was found. The crumbling legal system was merged with the overburdened police force, creating a powerful and efficient hybrid. These new guardians of society had the power to dispense both justice and punishment.

"They were police, jury and executioner, in one.

"They were . . .

"The Judges . . ."

EXT. THICK WALL – IN THE WASTELAND – SUNSET

Nothing grows here. Nothing could. This is the CURSED EARTH. With a whirr, a shuttle appears in the sky, flying to a giant city wall. A mammoth gate chugs open and the shuttle enters.

INT. WALL – SUNSET

As the massive craft settles, it is sprayed down by high-powered jets. Brown dirt drips away to show eroding metal and a logo underneath.

Previous page: The heavily fortified wall surrounding Mega-City One dates from the period of the Great Robot Wars. This exterior view by Matt Codd evokes the pure repressive force of the metropolis.

Opposite top: Nigel Phelps adds the telling detail of bristling gun emplacements to the Mega-City fortifications.

The earliest conceptions of the docking bay were for something bigger and more impersonal than the scheme that was finally used. Here, a design by Nigel Phelps (above) is rendered in ink by Matt Codd (left).

Above: *A fully rendered sketch of the less impersonal final version of the docking bay, which incorporates decorative design motifs carried over from the major city buildings. Notice the all-important eagle logo over the door.*

"MEGA-CITY JUDGE SYSTEM – ASPEN PRISON SHUTTLE # 3."

PUBLIC ADDRESS SYSTEM: (booming) "Aspen Prison shuttle docked. Commence anti-contamination. Spray down parolees. Prepare to disembark."

The shuttle's airlock port whooshes open. Drably dressed men and women emerge, carrying their few possessions.

The last convict in line is HERMAN FERGUSON ("FERGIE"), a genius without common sense, street smarts, or muscle tone. His career as a master criminal has gone nowhere. A GUARD checks him as he passes through a corridor.

GUARD: "Ferguson, Herman. Six-month sentence Aspen Prison served. Welcome back, citizen. Your living assignment is Block Y, Heavenly Haven, Red Quad. Next!"

Fergie hurries past the guard and exits at the end of the corridor – where he stops in his tracks, reacting to: A MAGNIFICENT CITY. Its giant towers reach miles into the sky. Elevated skyways are clogged *with traffic. Flying barges and shuttles service the highest levels. Almost lost and forgotten among the towering buildings is a tiny relic from our own time: the Statue of Liberty.*

Below: A sequence of storyboard drawings by Kevin Walker illustrating the docking of the Aspen Prison shuttle at the opening of Judge Dredd.

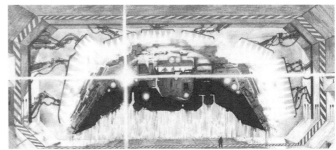

ON-SCREEN TITLE: "MEGA-CITY ONE: 2139"

Fergie looks up hopefully at the gleaming city, then down at his papers.

FERGIE: "Heavenly Haven. Sounds nice."

EXT. THE STREET IN FRONT OF HEAVENLY HAVEN BLOCK – SUNSET

And it is nice – a perfect Utopian future of happy families strolling through a green park. And then we realize that this scene is just a "video poster" plastered onto the side of a bleak tower block.

VIDEO POSTER: (taped voice over) "Coming soon, the Heavenly Haven Pocket Park. Bringing fresh air and recreation to your lives. Another design for better living from the Mega-City Council!" (pause) "Coming soon, the Heavenly Haven Pocket Park. Bringing fresh air . . ." (the pitch repeats in an endless loop)

Left: *A reference drawing of Mega-City One from the air.*

Below: *The first drawing by Kevin Walker of Mega-City One. It was thought to be too much of a fantasy city and not hard-edged enough to use.*

Right: *At the city wall's interior base, some artifacts of old New York are still visible. Simon Murton created this amazingly detailed cityscape, complete with imposing eagle motif over the main entrance. The look of official Mega-City owes more than a little to Albert Speer's grandiose plans for Nazi Berlin.*

Right: *Art department drawings of the upper levels of Mega-City structures equipped with acid rain shields.*

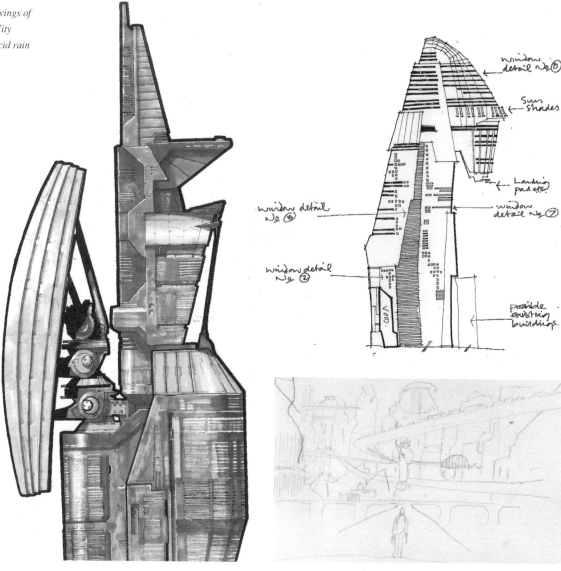

window detail №⑧

sun shades.

window detail № ⑥

Landing pad etc.

window detail № ⑦

window detail № ②

possible existing buildings.

Above right: *Director Danny Cannon's sketch of the all-important first image of Mega-City One, as Fergie returns home. Note that the Statue of Liberty is now right in the heart of the city, because the East River is all land-fill.*

Right: *Kevin Walker elaborates upon Cannon's basic design.*

Above: *A rendition of the Mega-City skyline with the recognizable modern-day Manhattan skyline superimposed by Martyn John.*

Left: *In this elaboration of Cannon's basic design, Nigel Phelps drew the background. The Fergie figure is an overlay by Kevin Walker.*

The three levels of Mega-City One are social and economic as well as architectural. The higher your rank and paycheck, the higher (and cleaner) your dwelling. Simon Murton adds dizzying layers of detail to the Mega-City-scape.

The Block War as originally conceived by Kevin Walker. In the foreground, Judge Dredd arrives on the scene.

Surrounding the block on all sides are giant tenements looming into the sky. Some local residents, or "Rezzies", scurry past, tired, hungry, dirty.

Suddenly, with a flicker, the commercial is turned off and replaced with the official eagle emblem of the Mega-City Judges. A small man in overalls, a city tech, slips a new disc into the poster's base. Rezzies gather round as it begins to play again.

The video poster now shows a grim monolithic building.

VIDEO POSTER: "Coming soon, the Heavenly Haven Law Enforcement Barracks, bringing surveillance and security to your lives. Another design for better living from the Mega-City Council."

As this sinks in, the Rezzies grow restive.

FIRST RESIDENT: "I don't believe it! They stole our park!"

SECOND RESIDENT: "Those lying bastards!"

FIRST RESIDENT: "Lying Judges!"

The video screen is shattered by a flying brick. The Rezzies swarm around it, tossing bricks and bottles.

INT. HEAVENLY HAVEN BLOCK –
SQUATTERS' APARTMENT – DUSK

An angry-looking punk named TWIST watches the riot from the window. Amused, he turns to four other crazed-looking squatters sitting around the grungy condemned room.

TWIST: "Hey, Droogs. The Rezzies are going mental."

The squatter leader, ZED, has a mad look in his eye.

ZED: "Perfect, let's give 'em a hand."

He motions to another squatter, REGGIE, who smiles and lifts up a mattress to reveal a cache of nasty futuristic weapons.

INT. TAXI SHUTTLE – IN FLIGHT ABOVE THE CITY – DUSK

Fergie is jammed in with several other low-rent passengers. The city is an awe-inspiring sight. As far as the eye can see, bizarre skyscrapers stab through thick smog.

Fergie sees a penthouse pool where some sexy girls are frolicking. He grins and waves.

FERGIE: (to the shuttle pilot) "Right down there. That's gotta be Heavenly Haven."

No such luck. The craft descends past the penthouse, deep into the dark bowels of the city. The structures it passes grow older. Filth and grime cover everything. The shuttle lands on the street with a whoosh.

EXT. THE STREET OUTSIDE THE HEAVENLY HAVEN BLOCK – DUSK

The second Fergie steps out of the shuttle, it lifts off. He looks around with a sigh.

FERGIE: "Still, better than prison."

Suddenly a brick sails past his head, missing him by centimeters. He looks down and is astonished to sees a chaotic urban riot in full swing! More and more of the frustrated Rezzies are throwing bricks, bottles, and garbage.

VOICES: (yelling) "They stole our park!" (chanting) "Block war! Block war! Block war!"

Dodging airborne debris, Fergie dashes into the building.

INT. HEAVENLY HAVEN BLOCK – CORRIDOR – NIGHT

A battered robot food cart cruises the hallway, oblivious to the people darting all around.

ROBOT FOOD CART: (a recording) "Delicious and healthful ration packs, piping hot and ready to eat."

Fergie checks his papers, moves toward "his" apartment. The door is ajar. Something's not right.

INT. SQUATTERS' APARTMENT – NIGHT

Fergie enters – and goes bugeyed as Zed jams a gun right between his eyes.

ZED: "What do we have here? You a Judge Spy, little man?"

The other squatters laugh at the concept.

A view of the main Block War street by Matt Codd with white streaks of gunfire helpfully added. This vast exterior set at England's Shepperton Studios went through several major re-dressings and is unrecognizable when it appears again later in the film. The Judges were added on an overlay.

Matt Codd rendered this complex early version of the Block War street. The section of the city above the elevated highway would have been supplied by a matte painting or miniature.

Below: *Matte design by Nigel Phelps drawn for Mass.Illusion to show where the matte line begins.*

Bottom: *Kevin Walker's rendition of the mid-town level drawn when the film was going to have three levels.*

FERGIE: "Me, no, no." (showing his papers) "I live in this apartment, I mean, I'm gonna live here. If I live." (trying to slip way) "Maybe I'll just go to a hotel–"

TWIST: "No way, man. Don't you hear them out there? It's a block war, man!!"

They grab him, playing roughly with him.

ZED: "If you're a Rezzie you gotta stand up for your block!"

FERGIE: "Look, I'm on parole. If I get in trouble my ass is back in Aspen."

Zed's gun is right back in his face.

FERGIE: (quickly, cheerleading) "Let's go, Haven! Let's go, Haven! Haven all the way."

Zed throws him to his friends, goes to the window.

ZED: (shouting) "BLOCK WAR!"

In madness and all together, they spew out bullets.

EXT. HEAVENLY HAVEN BLOCK – STREET LEVEL

Mayhem on the street. Falling concrete and explosions caused by the powerful weaponry. A Rezzie breaks for cover and is cut down in the middle of the street.

INT. HEAVENLY HAVEN BLOCK – THE SQUATTERS' APARTMENT

ZED: "Did you see that! What a shot!"

The squatters spread out across the window-sills and fire across at adjoining windows, down into the street. The opposite tower block begins to fire back. Pure chaos.

EXT. STREET LEVEL – NIGHT

Two figures speed toward the chaotic tower blocks, wearing armored uniforms, riding armored Lawmaster motorcycles that make Harleys look like mopeds. Both riders in visored helmets that conceal most of their faces. But the leader is unmistakably a woman. Her badge says "HERSHEY".

Left and below: A storyboard sequence created by Robbie Consing in 1993 showing the arrival of Hershey and Brisco at the Block War.

Below left: A conceptual sketch by Kevin Walker of the interior corridor of the Block War apartment buildings.

Bottom left: A fully rendered view of the Block War corridors by Simon Murton.

Various interior views of the Block War apartments by Simon Murton. The molded, "modular" Krupp coffee-maker look of the surfaces and furnishings represents mass-produced housing for the masses as practised in Mega-City One. Similar shapes were used for various futurist appliances in the film. Everything has been produced on the same assembly line.

Bullets ping around her.

HERSHEY: "Take cover!"

As bullets seek them out, the riders skid to a stop and jump behind their bikes, into combat positions. Hershey's partner, BRISCO, is young and eager. Too eager.

BRISCO: "It's just like an Academy simulation,
right down to the crossfire."

He starts to rise–

BRISCO: "I'll lead off, you follow."

HERSHEY: (yanking him back) "This isn't a sim, rookie! You will stand down and wait for back-up!" (into helmet mike) "In position outside Heavenly Haven. Under fire from upper floors."

EXT. A BUSY CITY STREET

In the shadows, a lone figure steps into the light to mount his Lawmaster bike. The rider's black-gloved hand activates the Lawmaster's backlit city map.

HERSHEY: (voice over, from the speakers on the bike) "Fire is coming from Level Y, repeat Y. Request back-up, nearest Judge!"

The map beeps, and displays a route. The gloved hand moves to the throttle, and pumps it.
 The Lawmaster roars forward, burning rubber, throwing up a cloud of blue smoke.

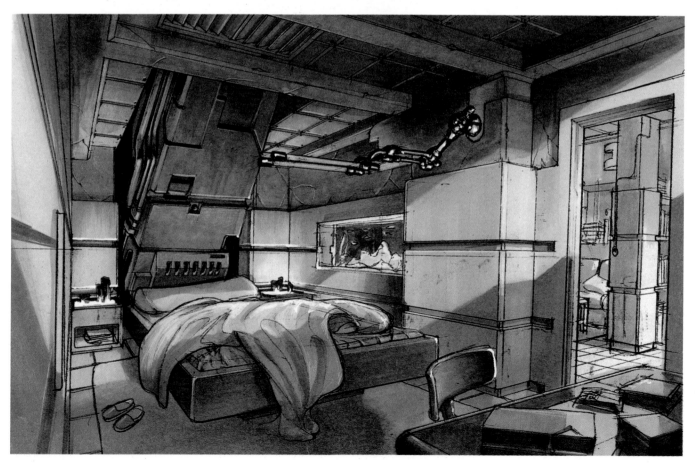

An interpretation of Diane Lane as Judge Hershey. This effect was achieved by Fleetway comic book artist Dermot Power by painting over a photograph.

EXT. STREET OUTSIDE HEAVENLY HAVEN – NIGHT

Smoke fills the street. The sounds of automatic weapons fire, exploding glass, and screams fill the air.

Hershey and Brisco are pinned down by a barrage of gunfire. Hershey tries to get off a shot as a bullet screams off the pavement nearby.

The oncoming Lawmaster whips around a corner, dodging a burned-out vehicle. A Molotov cocktail explodes on the pavement in front of the bike, which parts the flames like a curtain and slams to a halt right in the middle of the chaos.

The rider gets off the bike . . .

Hershey and Brisco huddle behind their bikes at the perimeter.

BRISCO: "Who the hell's that? He's a sitting duck out there."

He starts to rise. Hershey stops him with a hand on his shoulder.

HERSHEY: (smiling) "Sit back and pay attention, kid. He knows what he's doing."

The biker steps out of the flames.

Six feet of armored justice, his face concealed by his official visored helmet.

On his eagle-shaped badge the word "DREDD".

BRISCO: (with actual awe) "Holy shit . . ."

Dredd takes the microphone from his Lawmaster and his amplified voice fills the city canyon.

DREDD: "Drop your weapons! This block is under arrest!"

Amazingly, in an instant, there is calm. Silence. Hershey has to smile. Brisco can't believe his eyes.

INT. SQUATTERS' APARTMENT – NIGHT

Twist stares through his gunsight down at the street. In the gunsight, he sees Dredd's badge. He jumps back, terrified.

TWIST: "It's Judge Dredd!"

The others look at each other in stunned silence.

ZED: "What are you doing!?"

TWIST: (shitting his pants) "But it's . . . it's Dredd!"

Zed grabs Twist and slaps his face.

ZED: "Wanna be scared, be scared of me."

FERGIE: "How about if I run down there and surrender? Sorta throw him off guard."

All three squatters stare back at him. No way.

ZED: (shouting out the window) "Come and get us, Dredd, you pussy!"

He fires out the window. Inspired, Reggie happily joins in, then the others. Finally Twist shrugs and fires too.

EXT. THE STREET – NIGHT

The chaos starts up again. Gunfire pings off the pavement at Dredd's feet.

BRISCO: "Judge Dredd. Take cover!"

Dredd strides calmly over to Hershey and Brisco.

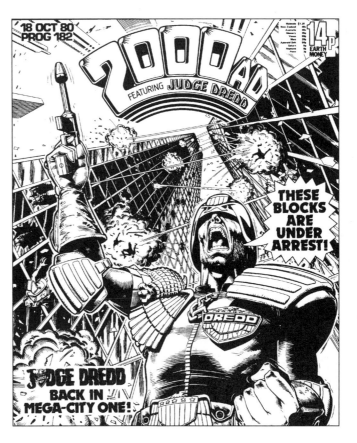

Opposite:
Simon Murton drafted these before and after images of a Heavenly Haven apartment that gets caught in the crossfire of the Block War.

A scene of a Block War from the pages of 2000AD.

DREDD: "He's firing 20mm caseless flechet rounds at six hundred feet–"

DREDD: "Effective lethal range is thirteen meters. We're safe.What are you doing back there, Judge Hershey?"

HERSHEY: "Waiting for back-up."

DREDD: "It's here."

Hershey and Brisco stand.

DREDD: (looking up at the building) "Let's go. Keep it simple. Standard relay. Single file. I'm point."

Hershey nods. Brisco, eager to prove himself, steps in front of Dredd at Heavenly Haven entrance. Dredd stops him with the back of his hand.

DREDD: "You? Last."

Brisco gets behind Hershey. Dredd turns toward Heavenly Haven as he draws his massive Lawgiver handgun. He speaks into a tiny computer in the breech as he aims at the door.

DREDD: "Grenade."

INT. HEAVENLY HAVEN – FRONT RECEPTION AREA – NIGHT

The door is blown off its hinges. Silhouetted in the doorway, the three Judges enter, Dredd moving ahead.

DREDD: "They're on the forty-eighth floor. Meet me there."

HERSHEY: (confused) "What you gonna do, ring the bell and ask them to stop?"

But he's already gone.

INT. HEAVENLY HAVEN – WITH THE SQUATTERS

Fergie, terrified, passes loaded ammo clips to his "friends". The whirr of a motor outside in the hallway attracts his attention: the food robot on its rounds.

FOOD ROBOT: "Delicious and healthful ration packs, piping hot and ready to eat!"

Fergie looks at his crazed "friends" and then back at the robot . . .

Opposite: A painted-over photograph of Sly Stallone as Judge Dredd by Dermot Power.

An interpretation of the Judge Dredd uniform by Italian designer, Gianni Versace.

INT. ANOTHER ROOM

The squatters are so busy firing their own guns out the window that they don't see the circle of bullet holes that carves an opening above their heads. With a crash, a section of ceiling falls and Dredd rides it down, firing two guns!

The squatters turn too late. Dredd's shots catch most of them by surprise. They fly backwards like rag dolls, until only their smoldering remains lie crumpled on the floor.

The door bursts open. Hershey and Brisco swing in, ready for battle. Dredd is calm.

DREDD: "This room . . . is pacified."

IN HALL NEAR DOOR TO THE NEXT ROOM

Dredd moves along the wall. Suddenly Brisco darts forward.

BRISCO: "This one's mine!"

HERSHEY: "No!"

Dredd tries to stop him, but he's too far away. Brisco kicks the door open.

INSIDE THE ROOM

Brisco is face to face with Reggie, Zed, and Twist.

BRISCO: "This room is under–"

Brisco is blown backwards off his feet. His Lawgiver goes flying, into the apartment, sliding across the floor toward Twist.

Hershey and Dredd go to Brisco, but it's obvious he's dying.

BRISCO: "D-Dredd . . . stupid uh . . ."

He's dead. Dredd's face hardens like rock.

INSIDE THE ROOM

TWIST: (suddenly noticing Brisco's gun) "A Lawgiver! Awesome!"

ZED: "Hey. Where's the little ammo dude?"

DREDD: (his voice from outside) "You're all under arrest. Surrender now, or prepare to receive your sentence."

The squatters glance at each other, shrug, then blast away. Dredd speaks again into the Lawgiver's computer.

DREDD: "Full auto. Rapid fire."

INSIDE THE ROOM

Twist picks up Brisco's Lawgiver and aims it at the doorway.

TWIST: "Come and get it, Judges!"

ZED: "Don't! It's booby-trapped!"

Too late. When Twist pulls the trigger an alarm

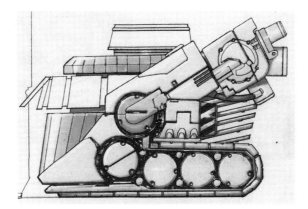

sounds three times and the Lawgiver explodes, shredding his flesh.

Dredd dives through the open door. His Lawgiver spews death.

Dredd rolls across the floor, the Lawgiver spewing bullets into the squatters' legs. He gets up, dives for cover, firing as Reggie fires a huge weapon, obliterating Dredd's hiding place.

DREDD: (into Lawgiver) "Armor-piercing!"

The weapon beeps and its LED display changes.

The bullet drills right through Reggie's weapon, killing him!

The other two squatters charge Dredd from either side.

DREDD: (to the Lawgiver) "Double whammy!"

The gun beeps.

Dredd fires. Two bullets blast out at once, cross in mid-air so that each takes out a man.

Zed starts to get up and sees Twist's severed arm lying on his chest. He screams and kicks it aside and jumps up, right into Dredd's kick.

Brisco is dead in Hershey's arms. She looks into the room where Dredd is dealing with Zed. But something catches her eye: Reggie isn't dead. He's reaching for a weapon, ready to shoot Dredd in the back. Hershey swings around with her Lawgiver drawn. When Reggie squeezes the trigger, Hershey takes him out.

DREDD: "Mega-City Municipal Code 334.8. Willful destruction of property. That's two years."

Zed searches for a weapon in a panic.

DREDD: "Code 11-5C. Illegal possession of assault weapons. Five years."

Dredd moves towards Zed with unnerving calm.

DREDD: "Code 34-A. Resisting arrest. Twenty years."

Zed is backed up against the window, but smiles confidently as Dredd gets closer.

DREDD: "9804. Assault on a Judge with deadly intent."

Zed has another weapon hidden behind his back.

ZED: (tough, scornful) "Don't tell me. Life."

Left and below: The automated food robot that was used as an escape vehicle by Fergie during the Block War.

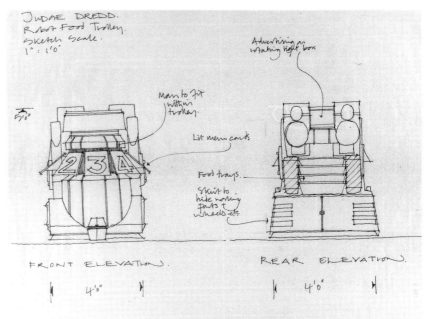

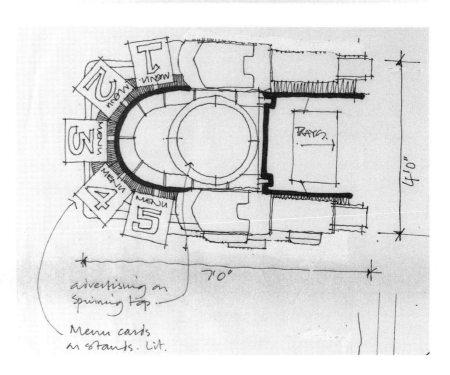

DREDD: "No. Death."

Dredd pulls the trigger and Zed flies back and crashes through a window. His scream lasts a long time before we hear a screech of tires forty-eight stories below.

Right: *The all-but-inexhaustible Block War machine gun.*

Below: *The Block War laser pump rifle, the choice of the perps, not the cops.*

Bottom: *The Block War pump rifle, a high-tech riot gun.*

DREDD: "Court . . . is adjourned."

INT. HEAVENLY HAVEN CORRIDOR – NIGHT

Judges process suspects and paramedics tend to the wounded. Hershey and Dredd look on as Brisco's body is lifted and carried away.

HERSHEY: "I was supposed to watch out for him. Damn it!"

DREDD: "Don't blame yourself, Hershey. He made the mistake, not you. His reactions were slow, his judgment faulty."

HERSHEY: (angry) "Oh, that's great. That makes me feel a lot better. Wouldn't it be okay to have an emotion once in a while?"

But Dredd is distracted. He cocks his head, listening. Somehow in the din and confusion he has heard something. He turns:
    The food robot is coming down the corridor, skittering around bodies and debris. Its actions are less smooth than before.

ROBOT VOICE: "Ummm, umm, yumm! Healthful and nutritious food rations, ready to eat."

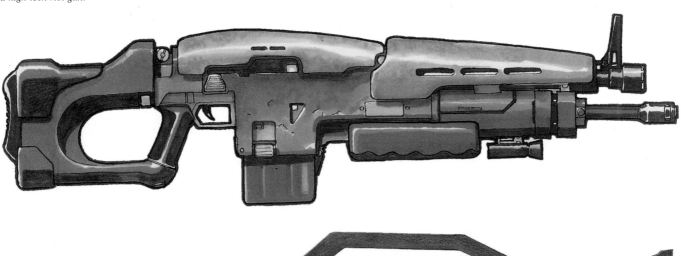

Dredd moves around in front of the robot, blocking its path.

DREDD: (to robot) "Halt! You have ten seconds to surrender. Ten. Nine."

HERSHEY: (puzzled) "Dredd, it's just a servo-droid . . ."

ROBOT VOICE: "Ah, just make your selection, insert your credit card in the slot and–"

Dredd suddenly pulls out his weapon and shoves the muzzle into the credit slot.

ROBOT VOICE: "– and . . . shit!"

A jumble of food spills out as Fergie uncoils from the cramped interior, still holding the sparking wires he was using to manipulate the machine. Dredd picks Fergie up by the scruff of the neck and pins him against the wall.

DREDD: "Mega-City Municipal Code 1286.4. Willful sabotage of a public droid. That's six months, citizen. Let's see your Unicard."

FERGIE: "Come on, give me a break, Judge uh–" (seeing name-tag, pales) "D-dredd? Oh God . . ."

Fergie swoons. By now Hershey has run her scanner over Fergie's card and Fergie's dossier is zipping by.

HERSHEY: "Ferguson, Herman. Hacker. Illegal tampering with city droids and computers . . . cash machines, robot taxis–"

DREDD: "And you haven't even been out of jail for twenty-four hours." (to Hershey) "He's a habitual, Hershey. Automatic five-year sentence."

He sees Dredd's impassive face, turns to Hershey's more sympathetic one.

FERGIE: "Five years? No – no! I – I had no choice, Judge! They were killing each other up there . . . I had no choice . . ."

DREDD: "You could have gone out the window."

FERGIE: "Forty-eight floors? It's suicide!"

DREDD: "Maybe, but it's legal. Five years – Aspen Penitentiary. Case closed. Take him away."

Still protesting, Fergie's hauled away. Hershey looks at Dredd.

HERSHEY: "He might have been telling the truth. Haven't you ever heard of extenuating circumstances?"

DREDD: "I've heard it all, Hershey."

She looks at Dredd disappointedly.

Below: *The final version of the Block War machine gun #3.*

Bottom: *Two versions of the Block War handgun.*

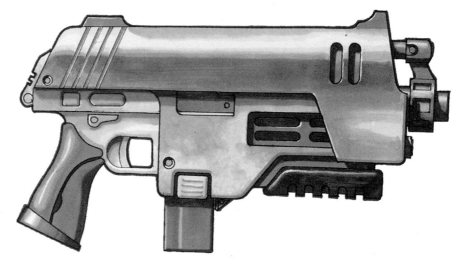

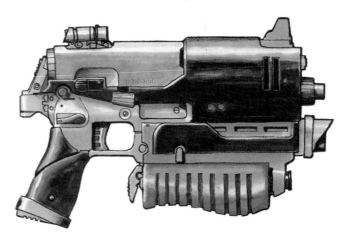

Danny Cannon and Nigel Phelps envisioned the Judges' headquarters building as a monumental Eagle of Justice. Kevin Walker worked up the first sketch.

EXT. HALL OF JUSTICE – NIGHT

The gleaming civil and legal heart of Mega-City, shaped like the symbol of the Judge System itself: an eagle.

VOICE: (GRIFFIN) "My fellow Judges, have we forgotten the lessons of History?"

INT. HALL OF JUSTICE COUNCIL CHAMBER – NIGHT

The Mega-City Council of Judges is in session. CHIEF JUSTICE FARGO, seventy, sits at an elevated position at a great black table.

In the center, a map of North America, showing only three Mega-Cities remaining: MC1 (New York); MC2 (L.A.); and Tex City (Houston). In the middle: the Cursed Earth.

Other Judges sit on either side of him. Among them are JUDGE MCGRUDER, a woman in her forties, open-minded but with an iron will; JUDGE ESPOSITO, also forties, thoughtful, accommodating; JUDGE SILVER, almost fifty, short-tempered, yet fair; and JUDGE GRIFFIN, sixty, with a mind and body as honed as men half his age, his clean features can hide much. But now, they hide nothing. His passion and sincerity make his words ring.

GRIFFIN: "However quickly these block wars can be contained, it is clear that they are becoming an epidemic. An epidemic that should be dealt with

immediately. The only solution is a tougher Criminal Code."

The assembly reacts as rowdily as the British Parliament.

SILVER: "The situation gets worse every day. Seventy-three citizen riots over two months in sixteen different sectors."

MCGRUDER: "Violent crime is rising 15 per cent every quarter. If we do not increase our resources, they will be inadequate in under three years."

ESPOSITO: "Three years? Our resources are inadequate now!"

An uproar. We sense that the room is evenly divided. A gavel bangs for order with a crack like thunder.

Above: *Nigel Phelps elaborates upon Kevin Walker's design.*

Left: *Director Danny Cannon drew this sketch to show that the Hall of Justice should not be too solitary or monolithic; he depicts it hemmed in closely by other Mega-City structures.*

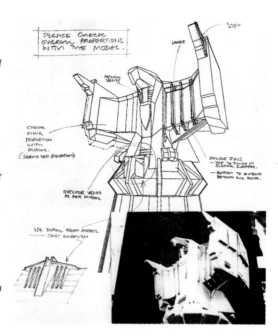

Right: *A model of the Hall of Justice by Martyn John.*

Far right: *Matt Codd's rendition of the Hall of Justice is closer to the final version.*

Below: *Kevin Walker's fully painted version of his Hall of Justice design.*

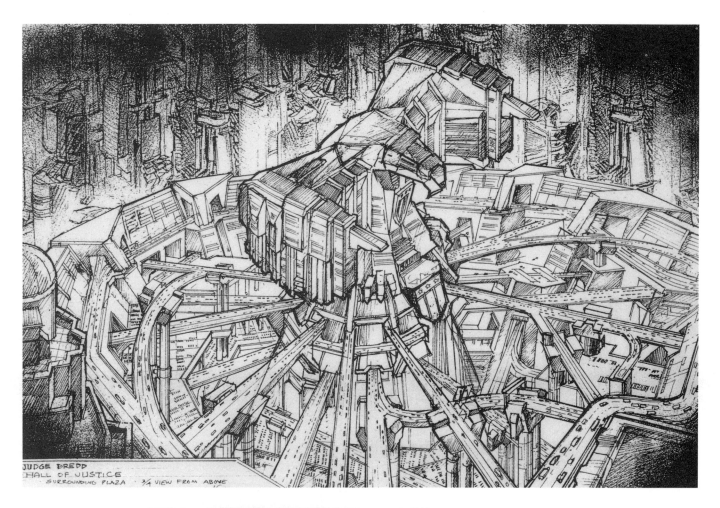

JUDGE DREDD
HALL OF JUSTICE
SURROUNDING PLAZA · ¾ VIEW FROM ABOVE

Above: A sketch of the more isolated version of the Hall of Justice by Bob Taylor, prepared by the Mass.Illusion team. The FX techs favored the more spacious design because it would have made effects sequences easier to integrate.

Above right: A sketch by Nigel Phelps of a proposed full-scale set of the entrance to the Hall of Justice.

FARGO: "My fellow council members. As a city, we continue to grow. And growth is painful. Sixty-five million people living in an area built for under twenty. It's not enough that they rely on us for clothes, food, water and clean air . . ."

GRIFFIN: (interrupting) "Chief Justice. This city is in chaos. For social order we need tighter reins. My curfew proposal should be implemented immediately."

FARGO: "Treat men like animals and they'll act like them."

GRIFFIN: "Perhaps you'd prefer we strip the Judges of their current powers and return to the antiquated system of trial and jury? Incarceration hasn't worked as a deterrent. I say we expand execution to include lesser crimes."

Fargo looks at the other Judges. He can see that Griffin is making sense to some of them.

FARGO: "This body is not the first assembly to think that more laws and fewer choices will bring peace and order. That delusion has been tried and failed before." (to Griffin) "My fellow Judges, I was barely in my teens when I put on this badge. When the time comes for me to take it off . . . let me do it knowing that it stood for Freedom . . . and not for Repression."

He sits down. Clearly he has changed the mood of the room. Griffin more than anyone understands and respects this.

GRIFFIN: "Once again, Chief Justice, you have served as a moral compass for all of us. I . . . withdraw my proposal." (pause) "I hope . . . for good."

INT. HALL OF JUSTICE – CORRIDOR – NIGHT

Dredd, helmet still on, is watching a monitor. VARDIS HAMMOND, grey-haired, commanding, is standing in front of Heavenly Haven while workers put things back in order.

HAMMOND: (on the monitor) "–fifty-three people hospitalized. Five of them . . . children. Nineteen, dead . . . four of them allegedly led by a gang of squatters who were themselves killed in summary executions by Judge Dredd . . ."

The Council Chamber doors open. Griffin comes over, watches with Dredd. Dredd stiffens at the approach of his superior. Griffin silently indicates for him to stand at ease.

DREDD: (grimly) "A rookie Judge died there today, too. I guess he wasn't worth mentioning."

GRIFFIN: (wryly) "No, that might confuse the viewers. We can't be victims, Dredd . . . we're the villains!"

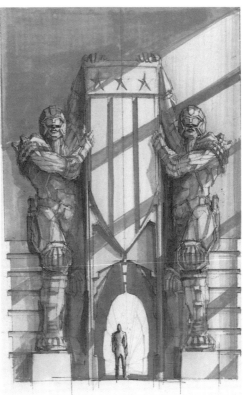

Above: *The influence of Ken Adam, the famed designer of most of the James Bond pictures, can be seen in the angled, circular shape of the ceiling in Simon Murton's wash drawing of the Judges' Council Chamber. Production designer Nigel Phelps is an avowed fan of Adam's work, and Murton's father worked as an illustrator with Adam for many years.*

Left: *Door in the corridor outside the Hall of Justice leading to the Academy by Simon Murton.*

DREDD: "Things will change, sir."

GRIFFIN: (leaving) "I pray for it every night, Dredd."

As Griffin leaves, Dredd turns back to the screen:

HAMMOND: "Some say that working these mean streets day after day is bound to have a dehumanizing effect on the Judges – but is it the streets or the Judges

themselves that have created this atmosphere of savagery? As my special undercover report continues tomorrow night I'll take you behind the walls of the Hall of Justice for a disturbing probe into these recent riots and block wars – coincidence or deliberate?"

FARGO: "Dredd!"

Dredd turns to see Fargo at the door to the chamber, beckoning him. Startled, Dredd steps inside.

INT. COUNCIL CHAMBER – NIGHT

Lights dim now that the session is over. The atmosphere is cathedral-like. Fargo stands in front of the bas-reliefs around the hall – tapestries of the wars, famines and violence that ruined our world.

DREDD: "Yes, Chief Justice?"

FARGO: "Joseph–"

Fargo is quiet, reflective. Dredd stands beside him.

FARGO: "As you know, I've always taken a special interest in your career."

Right: *A design sketch for a wall monitor by Julian Caldow.*

Below from left: *Costume designs for two Council members, a Council Judge's uniform and the Chief Judge's uniform.*

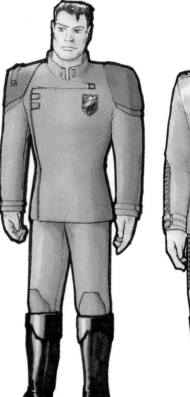
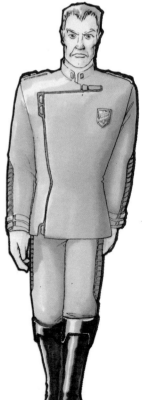

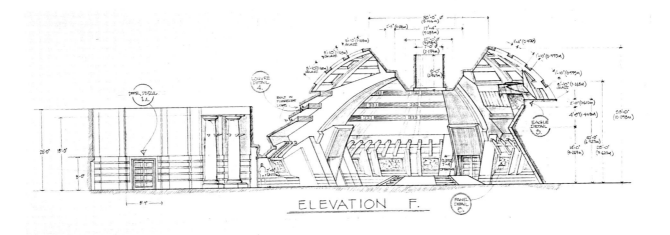

ELEVATION F.

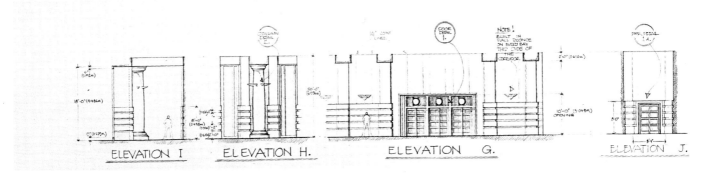

ELEVATION I   ELEVATION H.   ELEVATION G.   ELEVATION J.

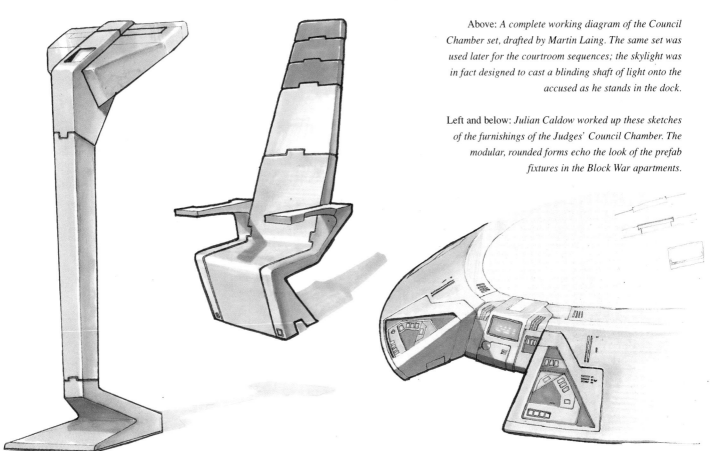

Above: A complete working diagram of the Council Chamber set, drafted by Martin Laing. The same set was used later for the courtroom sequences; the skylight was in fact designed to cast a blinding shaft of light onto the accused as he stands in the dock.

Left and below: Julian Caldow worked up these sketches of the furnishings of the Judges' Council Chamber. The modular, rounded forms echo the look of the prefab fixtures in the Block War apartments.

Above and opposite: *Chris Halls designed the historical mural that adorns the Council Chamber. These three sections depict the Robot Wars that delivered political power into the hands of the Judges.*

DREDD: "Yes, sir. I know that it's appreciated."

FARGO: "So tell me. Seven summary executions. Were they . . . necessary?"

Dredd does not avert his gaze.

DREDD: "Unavoidable, sir."

FARGO: "Unavoidable? We make our own reality, Dredd."

DREDD: "With all due respect, sir, times have changed: life doesn't mean much to some people any more. You would be able to see that if you weren't . . ."

FARGO: (sitting up) "If I weren't what?"

DREDD: "Always at the Academy . . . sir."

FARGO: "Don't you mean at the Academy wiping cadets' asses? That is what they say in the squad room, isn't it?"

DREDD: "It's irrelevant, sir. You set the standard."

FARGO: "No, you do, at least to many young cadets. You're a legend."

Fargo is playing with Dredd. He knows he hates a compliment.

DREDD: "Sir –"

Fargo gets close to Dredd.

FARGO: "Joseph, do you remember your time at the Academy?"

DREDD: "I remember what you taught me, sir."

Fargo manages to smile.

FARGO: "I remember a cadet who embraced Justice. The ideals as well as the lessons. My finest student. I've drawn a new assignment for you. Starting tomorrow you're going to spend two days a week at the Academy."

Dredd takes this in his stride.

DREDD: "I'd be honored. Unarmed combat, or marksmanship?"

FARGO: (standing, with a grin) "Ethics."

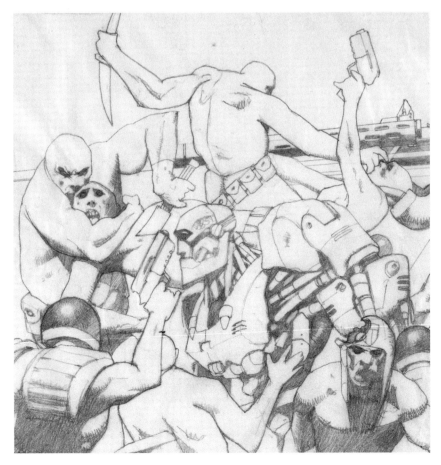

Above: *The Great Seal of the Judges, as drawn by Julian Caldow. The Latin slogan says, "An orderly populace is the supreme law."*

Various concepts for an exterior establishing shot of the Aspen Prison Colony that was eventually abandoned. The early version by Nigel Phelps (above) is based directly upon London's Battersea Power Station.

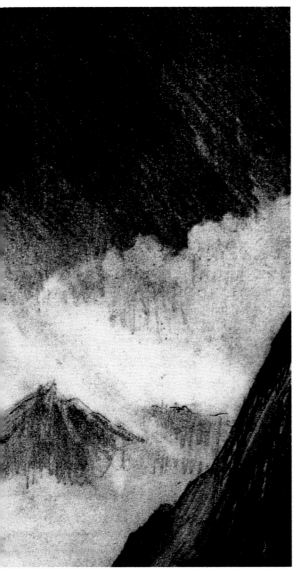

EXT. ASPEN PENAL COLONY – DAY

Through a violent blizzard we see an ominous mountain fortress. Guard towers on every corner. Wind rattles the concertina wire on the walls. If the Cursed Earth is hell, this is hell's prison.

INT. PRISON – CELLBLOCK – NIGHT

Row upon row of impenetrable grim steel cells. Accompanied by heavily armed security guards, the warden, JUDGE MILLER, strides through the complex.

INT. MAXIMUM SECURITY WING

Miller and two guards descend through the old part of the complex. Everything gets progressively dirtier and more dilapidated as they go. Finally, they reach a massive steel door with a computer access screen. Miller puts his hand on the lock.
The red light turns green. The door clicks open.

INT. RICO'S CELL – DAY

Miller steps inside. Autoguns mounted in the walls swing toward him. The door closes.

GUN COMPUTER: "Remain still. Identify yourself."

MILLER: "Miller. Warden."

GUN COMPUTER: "Voice sample recognized. Thank you, Warden."

The guns swing back, training their sights on a circular platform in the circular steel room. Blue light creates a circular platform around it; behind it, a figure moves.

RICO: (from darkness) "Warden. Have you come for another . . . chat?"

MILLER: "A short one, I'm afraid. Duty calls."

RICO: "You look tired, Miller. You must loathe this job – feeding parasites at the public's expense."

MILLER: "You especially."

Left: *Nigel Phelps drafted this intermediate version of Rico's cell, spectacular but still a bit too fancy to be functional.*

Below: *Rico's metallic bed/chair with reading light attached. It folds flat or at angles for sitting.*

Bottom: The *"Puzzle Gun" used by Rico to escape from the Aspen Prison Colony.*

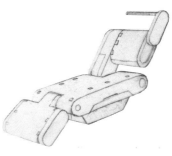

RICO: "Oh, I don't cost the taxpayer anything. I'm a ghost."

Rico moves into the light. A handsome man, who has kept himself in good shape; yet his eyes are crazed.

RICO: "We're both prisoners here. You behind a desk. Me behind . . . this. Fargo's reward for our services."

MILLER: "When you killed innocent people you went far beyond service."

RICO: "Innocent? The innocent exist only until they inevitably become perpetrators themselves. In the end, guilt and innocence are merely a matter of timing. And when did you become a perpetrator? When you conspired to keep me alive, or when you accepted bribes to keep things that way?"

MILLER: "Feel grateful. Your – our mysterious benefactor has sent you a package." (to computer) "Deactivate shield. Autoguns only."

The blue light fades as a warmer one replaces it. The autoguns on the wall swivel toward Rico. Miller moves onto the platform, hands over the package. Rico places his thumb on the lock and it snaps open.

Inside the package rests Rico's old Judge's badge, along with a photograph of Hammond, the

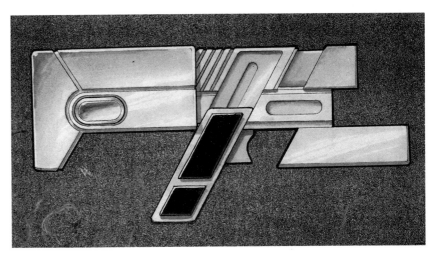

newscaster, and what appears to be a Rubik cube-style puzzle.

MILLER: (curious) "What is that?"

Rico begins to manipulate the puzzle.

RICO: "The Ancient Puzzle, containing the Meaning of Life."

MILLER: (sarcastic) "Really. So Rico, tell me, what is the meaning of life?

RICO: "It ends."

Opposite: *Early sky's-the-limit visual concepts for the Aspen Prison Colony. In Matt Codd's version (top), prisoners slouch along high catwalks toward a beehive arrangement of thousands of cells. Nigel Phelps's design (bottom) for the cellblock is more like a kennel than a facility for human beings. This is based on Bankside power station where the Aspen interiors were shot.*

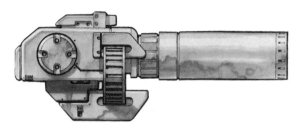

He points the "puzzle" at Miller. BLAM! The shot from the tiny weapon hits the warden in the throat. Gasping, Miller drops to his knees.

MILLER: (coughing) "Computer . . . ac-activate al-alarm!"

GUN COMPUTER: "Voice not recognized. Remain still."

Miller panics and scrambles for the door.

GUN COMPUTER: "Security Breach! Autoguns targeting!"

MILLER: "NO!"

Above: *Final version of the autoguns in Rico's cell by Julian Caldow.*

He's cut down ten feet from the door.

OUTSIDE THE DOOR

Right: *Matt Codd painted this spectacular early design for Rico's cell at the Aspen Prison Colony, mounted on gyroscopes and shielded by a force field. A less imposing but more functional look was eventually selected.*

The two guards jack shells into their riot guns. One punches "override" into the door's keypad. They charge inside.

In the cell the guards see only a body. They move slowly towards the platform to look down at it. They recognize Miller – as behind them Rico jumps up from under the walkway! The guards turn too late. Rico's hands grasp the first guard's head and twist. SNAP! Pulling the gun from the falling body Rico fires and the second guard sinks to his knees, shot cleanly between the eyes.

Below: *Nigel Phelps sketched the final version of Rico's maximum security cell at the Aspen Prison Colony.*

RICO: (smiles) "I'm back."

INT. ACADEMY – TRAINING RANGE – DAY

Bullets ricochet off a dummy's body armor.

DREDD: "Kevlar nine helmet and body armor."

Dredd is lecturing to a group of cadets who hang on his every word. We're in a training area like the one Q ran in the James Bond movies.

DREDD: "Yours, when you graduate." (pause) "If you graduate."

Dredd moves to another training station. Another tech nods.

DREDD: (holding up) "The Lawgiver Two. Twenty-five-round sidearm with mission-variable voice-programmed ammunition." (into gun) "Signal flare."

He fires. The flare explodes on the wall.

DREDD: "Yours, when you graduate."

At the supply room door, Hershey stands watching Dredd, impressed with his style. Dredd moves to several techs who are hurriedly tweaking the most awesome Lawmaster motorcycle we've ever seen.

DREDD: "Mark IV Lawmaster, improved model, with on-board dual laser cannons, vertical take-off and landing, flight capacity and 500-kilometer range."

The head tech gives thumbs-up while the other techs step back. The class waits, expectant. The lead tech throws a remote switch. The bike's wheels rise up into its body, leaving it hovering two foot from the ground. The bike computer reads "ACTIVE". It wobbles, then sparks fly. The motor coughs and dies. The wheels fold out again and it sits back down.

DREDD: "Yours . . . if they ever get it to work."

The cadets laugh as Dredd moves to a lectern. He faces the class.

DREDD: "All of these things are nothing but toys. End of the day, when you're alone in the dark, all that counts . . . is this."

He takes something from the lectern shelf, throws it down. It's the all-but-holy book: THE LAW.

DREDD: "And you will be alone when you swear

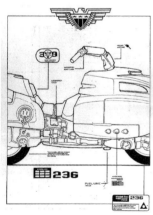

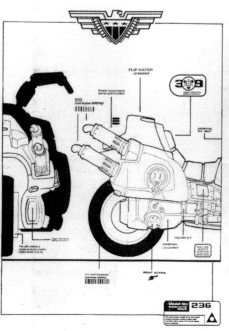

Above, right and far right: A series of drawings to be used in the film in the Justice Academy on the Lawmaster.

to uphold these ideals."

The cadets frown; this is not what they expected to hear from a living legend. They become increasingly unnerved.

The talk upsets Hershey, too, perhaps more than the others.

DREDD'S VOICE: "For most of us there is only death on the streets . . . or, for those few of us who survive to old age . . . the prouder loneliness of the Long Walk, into the unknown of the Cursed Earth, to spend your last days taking the law into the outlands." (pause) "Class dismissed."

The class breaks up on a definite low note.

INT. ACADEMY LOCKER ROOM – DAY

Hershey dries her hair with a towel. A short, earnest cadet named OLMEYER approaches her. He's carrying a large book.

OLMEYER: "Judge Hershey, the deadline is only a week away. Have you changed your mind?"

HERSHEY: "Forget it, Olmeyer. I am not going to be the yearbook centerfold!"

OLMEYER: "It's not a centerfold, it's a calendar! And it won't be a tacky 3-D hologram. The yearbook is all classic print and 2-D. Here, let me show you a dummy–"

HERSHEY: "No, I'll show you one."

She turns him towards the polished locker wall. He faces his own reflection. Some other cadets snigger.

Dredd stands in the shadows removing his helmet. Hershey watches him take off his jacket, his tight muscle-bound body riddled with scars. There is a Judge emblem tattooed on his shoulder, like her own. He fascinates her. Finally, she approaches him. As she gets close, Dredd stops and half-turns to her, his face shadowed.

HERSHEY: "Judge Dredd? I caught your lecture today. Do . . . do you really think that's what the cadets need to hear?"

He looks at her for a second, but she can only see pieces of him in this light.

DREDD: "I told them the truth."

Above and opposite page, top:
Front and back views of the Lawmaster by Simon Murton.

Opposite: *Two versions of a Justice Academy cadet's uniform. The final version (top) is slightly modified and in midnight blue.*

Left: *A painting of Judge Dredd and the Flying Lawmaster by Kevin Walker.*

Below: *An early concept of the Lawmaster traveling on the road and flying by Danny Cannon.*

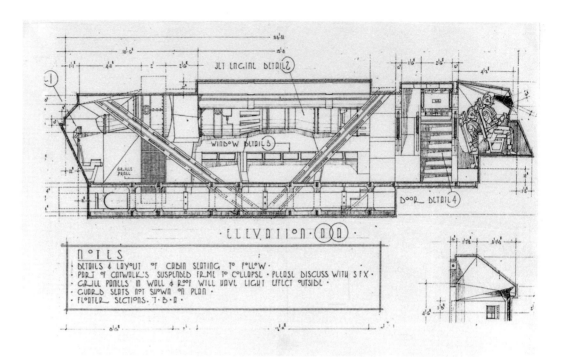

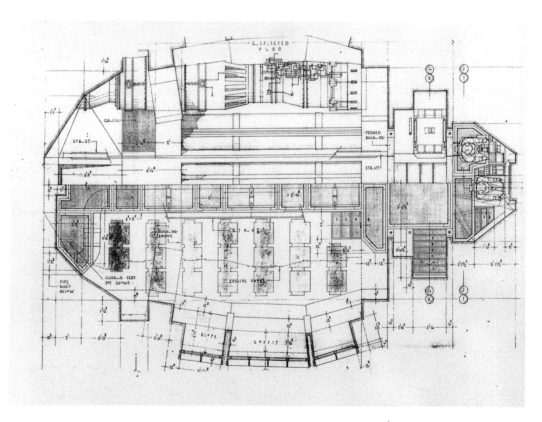

Right: *Two views of the shuttle that ferries prisoners to and from the Aspen Prison Colony by Peter Russell.*

HERSHEY: "Your truth, maybe. I've been on the streets a year and I still have a personal life. I have lots of friends."

He stops.

DREDD: "Really?"

HERSHEY: (defensively) "May I get personal?"

Dredd sighs. This is the last thing he needs right now.

HERSHEY: "Why have you never married?"

Dredd moves towards her, his face coming fully into the light. A scarred, battle-worn, hard face. His deep blue eyes look into her soul.

DREDD: "It wouldn't be fair, would it?"

HERSHEY: (beat) "Has it really been like that for you? Haven't you ever . . ." (checking herself) "Haven't you ever had a friend?"

DREDD: "Yes. Once."

HERSHEY: "Well, what happened?"

For a moment fleeting pain passes across Dredd's face. But before it can fully register on us, or Hershey, he walks away. Hershey gets the meaning.

HERSHEY: "You judged him."

She remains rooted to the spot.

EXT. MEGA-CITY WALL LOCK – NIGHT

An Aspen barge is docked here. It is dark, quiet.

INT. WALL – CORRIDOR – NIGHT

A crew member with a computer tablet checks off items as a guard ticks them off.

GUARD: "Two loads from the prison factory in Hold Number One, ore from the prison mine in Holds Number Three and Four, prisoner mail in Two."

CREW MEMBER: "And no prisoners?"

GUARD: "Just dead ones."

He gestures towards some body bags as he moves away.

GUARD: (leaving) "Their families were probably glad to get rid of them. Now they gotta bury them."

Alone now, the guard leans down to check the names on the bags. Suddenly, one of the body bags sits up, its face straining against the plastic. The guard reacts too late. A laser shoots out silently and the guard hits the floor. Rico slips out of the body bag.

Left: *The seating arrangement of the prison shuttle was modeled upon the Roman slave galleys in the film epic* Ben Hur, *a favorite of director Danny Cannon.*

Right: *A fully rendered painting by Kevin Walker of the red-light district. The designs had to suggest a seething den of vice and crime without going into too much explicit detail.*

Left and opposite bottom: *Two scenes by Matt Codd for an elaborate nightclub sequence featuring holographic nude dancers and other futuristic delights. The sequence was eventually abandoned.*

EXT. MEGA-CITY – NIGHT

Not a nice part of town. A busy, crowded red-light district. The faces and sounds are unnerving. This is not the shiny future we have been seeing now and again. This is the unlit shadow of that world.

Rico appears, wearing mix-and-match items from the wardrobes of the two men he's just killed. He walks past rows of men enraptured in violent/erotic video games. He looks around.

On a TV screen, the broadcaster Hammond. It's a replay of his block war segment. Rico smiles and looks up at a shop with a busy ever-changing sign: "GEIGER'S BAZAAR: SURPLUS – PAWN – FAX BOXES – VOUCHERS CASHED."

Rico heads inside.

INT. GEIGER'S BAZAAR – NIGHT

A large and squalid pawnshop. Junk hangs from the cluttered walls. The rear is divided by a ceiling-high locked fence that secures the better merchandise. The pawnbroker, GEIGER (mid-fifties), puffs on a cigar and scowls as Rico enters.

GEIGER: "We've closed for the night."

RICO: "You're holding a package for me. Code-name, Lazarus."

GEIGER: (nervous) "Oh, yeah . . . Gimme a second."

Geiger ducks out of sight and Rico quickly scans the store. A jumble of crates and large antique weapons. A simple security camera in the corner.

RICO: "Nice place."

GEIGER: "It might look like junk to most."

Rico points to what seem like rusting metal warriors.

RICO: "I thought they destroyed all the ABC warriors after the last war?"

GEIGER: (returning) "You can collect 'em if you make 'em non-functional. Like my wife. These guys must be fifty, sixty years old." (he hands Rico a box) "Here you go."

Geiger pretends not to watch as Rico opens the box with the thumb lock. Geiger sneaks a look. Inside, a Judge's uniform and Lawgiver sidearm. Rico starts

to reach into the box. Geiger stops him.

GEIGER: "Wait a second, don't touch it! Whoever sent you this is no friend at all."

RICO: "Oh? Why's that?"

GEIGER: "That's a Lawgiver. They're programmed to only recognize a Judge's hand prints. If you want a weapon I can get you something nice. But touch that and it'll take your arm off."

RICO: "Really?"

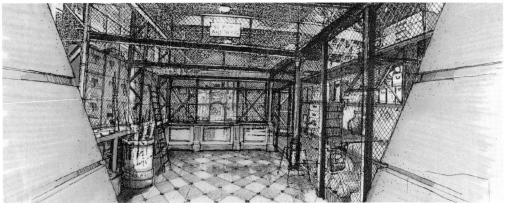

Above: *An external view of Geiger's gun shop by Kevin Walker.*

Left: *The interior of Geiger's grey-market gun shop went through several permutations before Nigel Phelps produced the final version. This one is by Les Tomkins.*

Rico suddenly grabs the gun. Geiger jumps back, then looks puzzled when nothing happens.

RICO: "How do you like that?"

He shoots Geiger at point-blank range. Geiger hits the floor.

RICO: "I must be a Judge."

Rico bends down, lifts Geiger's keys (and his cigars) then goes over to the big cage.

The ABC robot is a huge armored combat veteran. The metal cage rattles open and Rico enters, crouching down to pull a panel off the robot's head. Cables tumble from its temples like dreadlocks. Rico skillfully finds the right ones, pulling small steel tendons out, twisting one to another.

A spark, a flinch. The robot starts to whirr. A gush of steam rises from its powerful torso. The eyes glow red. Rico steps back as the robot turns like an arthritic old man. Inside, a computer's deep voice.

ABC ROBOT: "Status. Commander. Mission."

Rico strikes a match on the robot, lights a cigar.

RICO: "Status: personal bodyguard. Commander: Rico. Me. Mission:" (he smiles) "we're going to war."

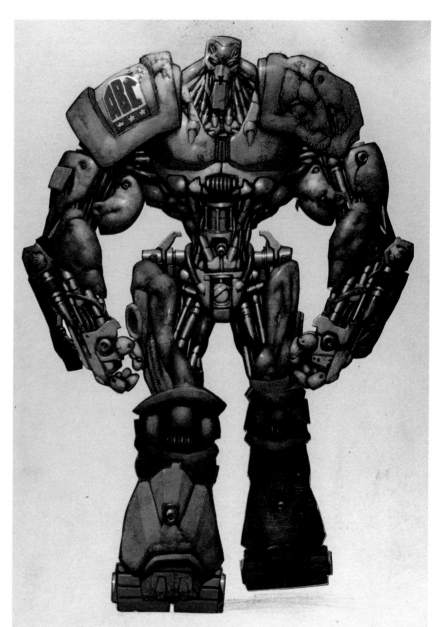

The final version (above) *is by Chris Halls as is the sketch* (left).

Rico's imposing robot sidekick as envisioned by Kevin Walker, who had drawn the character for the 2000AD comic book series "ABC Warriors". The basic shape dictated by the comics is embellished in various ways; notice differences in the jawline and chest and arm muscles from version to version.

This page:
Sketches of the Land Rover taxi drawn by Land Rover designer David Woodhouse.

Opposite far right from top:
Three sketches for the Mega-City SkyCab.

EXT. APARTMENT BLOCK – NIGHT

A tiny apartment complex dwarfed by the new construction swelling up around it.

LILY HAMMOND: (off screen) "That's seditious!"

INT. HAMMOND'S APARTMENT – NIGHT

Hammond and his wife Lily are in their modest apartment. Both wear nightclothes. Their antiques and decorations hint at a war era – our own. Hammond is writing at a tiny computer console.
Lily looks over his shoulder, shocked.

LILY: (reading from the screen) "A conspiracy in the justice system? Radical elements on the City Council? Where did you get this?"

HAMMOND: "When I followed up some grumblings coming from low-level Council pages I found they confirmed a suspicion of mine: that this cancer of oppression goes deeper than the street Judges."

LILY: (incredulous) "You're going to say that over the air?"

HAMMOND: "It's the truth."

LILY: "Vardis, you're insane."

HAMMOND: "I'm a reporter."

LILY: "That doesn't mean you have to get yourself killed."

HAMMOND: (laughs) "They don't kill reporters, Lily."

LILY: "They'll never let this get on the air. Something like this could bring down the Council!"

BONG! The quiet tone of the door chime. Hammond gets up and starts across the room.

HAMMOND: "Maybe it should come down. I was wrong to waste my time investigating individual Judges. The problem is the entire system . . ." (he reaches for the door handle) ". . . not just Judge Dredd."

The door swings open. A Judge is silhouetted in the opening.
BRANK! BRANK! The Judge's gun spews death.

EXT. MEGA-CITY STREET – DAY

A wet dream of a futuristic gull-winged car tries to ram its way out of a tight parking spot, crashing repeatedly into the cars in front and behind.

The driver is an obnoxious FUPPIE (Future Yuppie) with a hot date, who finds this funny.

FUPPIE: (drunk) "Wow! These ener-sorb bumpers are amazing! You can't feel a thing! Can you?"

As he turns to plow one more time into the car in front of him, he checks his wing mirror, adjusting it to see . . . Hershey, who stands calmly behind him.

HERSHEY: "Step out of the car, please."

FUPPIE: "What the hell is the problem now?"

Hershey flings open the gull-wing door and yanks the fuppie out by the arm.

HERSHEY: "Step out of the car. You can make it hard or easy. You too, Miss."

FUPPIE: (shaking free) "Hey, girl, maintain yourself! I got connections on the Council."

HERSHEY: "Unicard, please."

Hershey takes out the fuppie's unicard from his top pocket, and slides it through her scanner.

HERSHEY: "Did you hear me? I'm citing you for reckless driving." (consults instrument) "Mr . . . De Souza." (looks up) "You have a suspended license. Three counts of driving under the influence."

FUPPIE: "You better listen up. Whatever your name is. I suggest you walk away and bother somebody else. When I said I have powerful friends, I mean powerful."

Bottom left: *The film's designers created several alternative plans for the obnoxious "fuppie's" (Future Yuppie) flashy vehicle. The gull-winged final version resembles a Ferrari on steroids.*

Bottom right: *A beautifully rendered line diagram by Julian Caldow of the final version of the FuppieMobile.*

Above: *An early design for the Land Rover taxi by Kevin Walker.*

Opposite top: *An actual piece of British military hardware, the Saracen Armored Vehicle, was modified to serve as an all-purpose official Mega-City Justice Department runabout.*

Opposite left: *A drawing of the modified Saracen by Julian Caldow.*

He stops suddenly, feeling a large chest behind him – he turns to read another Judge's badge: "DREDD".

DREDD: "Are we having a problem here, Hershey?"

HERSHEY: "Not at all, Dredd. I can handle it. Suspended license and three D.U.I.s."

FUPPIE: "This is getting boring. Okay, what's the tab? How much is this going to cost me? Name your price."

DREDD: "You wanna suck on my fist, creep? Say that again." (to Hershey) "Hershey, call Control for an H-wagon."

FUPPIE: "What, are you taking me in? I want my car towed to a safe place."

DREDD: "Towing is the penalty for the first offense. This is your fourth violation. You're a menace. How do you plead?"

FUPPIE: "Not guilty."

DREDD: "I knew you'd say that. You want it moved?"

Dredd draws his Lawgiver.

DREDD: (speaks into the Lawgiver) "Grenade."

FUPPIE: "No!"

Dredd aims, fires, and the car explodes. The fuppie and his date stand slack-jawed as debris tinkles down around them.

Hershey is not surprised. She turns, seeing dark figures through the flames.

DREDD: "Anything else you want moved?"

HERSHEY: "I love your subtlety."

DREDD: "He broke the law."

HERSHEY: "What do they want?"

Dredd turns to look at the dark figures.

DREDD: "Judge Hunters!"

They are garbed for combat, without even the trace of humanity that seeps through the armor of a Street Judge. These are the feared JUDGE HUNTERS. All have drawn weapons. The leader holds up a Holo Warrant with Dredd's picture.

JUDGE HUNTER LEADER: "Judge Joseph Dredd. You are under arrest."

DREDD: "Arrest? The Judge Hunters have made a mistake."

JUDGE HUNTER: "Don't move, Dredd."

HERSHEY: "What's the charge?"

JUDGE HUNTER LEADER: "Murder."

Dredd is stupefied.

Above: *An early design for a Judge Hunter's uniform by Julian Caldow.*

Left: *Two versions of the Judge Hunter's helmet by Little John.*

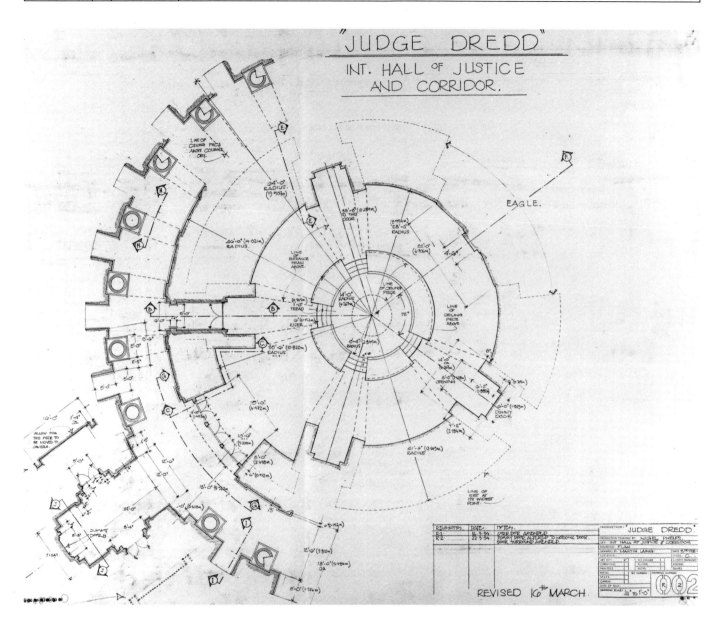

Above: *Elevation of the interior Hall of Justice and corridor drawn by Martin Laing.*

Opposite top: *Elevation of the Academy locker room drawn by Martin Laing.*

Opposite left: *Elevation of the Academy training range drawn by Martin Laing.*

Opposite right: *Various possibilities of Academy doors drawn by Nigel Phelps.*

INT. JUDGES' COMPLEX – CELL CORRIDOR – DAY

At this hour the complex is quiet, empty. The Judge Hunters usher Chief Justice Fargo to an open holding cell.

INT. HOLDING CELL – DAY

Fargo arrives at the cell and sees Dredd sitting on the side of the bed, manacled into a set of nearly transparent chains, a cell of steel-hard plastic. The Hunters move away.

FARGO: (formal) "Joseph."

Dredd rises in respect. He is surprisingly calm.

DREDD: "Sir?"

FARGO: "Is it true?"

DREDD: "I'm innocent."

FARGO: "The Council is said to have irrefutable proof. There's to be a full tribunal."

DREDD: "Do you believe them?"

They look into each other's eyes, each afraid of the truth they might find there. After a long beat, Fargo's face relaxes, reassured, and his fondness for Dredd pours out.

FARGO: "I'm sorry I had to ask. I just needed to

look into your eyes for myself."

They look at each other with loyalty and affection.

DREDD: "How could this happen? I don't understand."

FARGO: "I'll use every resource to find out. Have you selected a colleague to defend you?"

DREDD: "I've asked Judge Hershey."

FARGO: (dubious) "Hershey? Why a Street Judge?"

Dredd is to the point – as usual.

DREDD: "I can trust her."

Fargo rises to leave. The Judge Hunters unlock the cell.

FARGO: "The facts will come out at the tribunal. I'll make sure of that."

Fargo manages an encouraging smile – and leaves.

EXT. CELL

When Dredd can no longer see him, Fargo's smile drops away, betraying his dire concern.

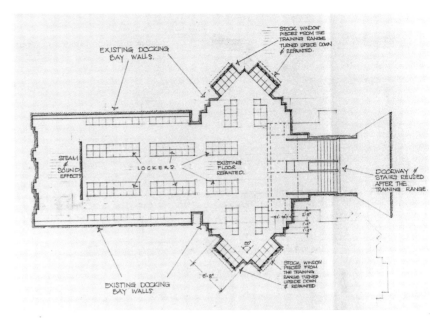

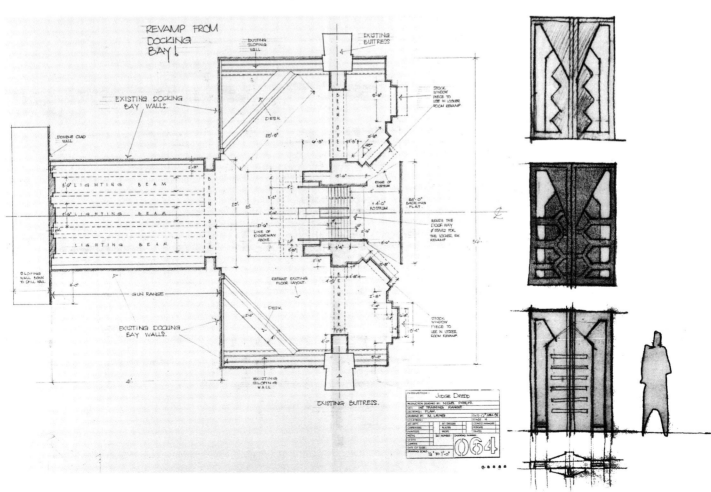

Simon Merton's sketch of a virtual reality theater in the Academy. This scene was going to involve a street simulation with Dredd and his class. In the end it was not used.

INT. COUNCIL CHAMBER – NIGHT

HAMMOND ON VIDEO: "Dredd, no please –"

An explosion of gunfire on the main screen. This is the tail-end of a surveillance video of the murders of the Hammonds, taken by a camera outside their apartment.

JUDGE MCGRUDER'S VOICE: "Stop video."

Hershey stands nervously beside Dredd. This is the first time she has seen the tape. An enormous weight sits on her shoulders today.

The Council Chamber is absolutely packed. Every off-duty Judge in Mega-City is here. So is every cadet from the Academy plus the entire media corps. On the center dais stands Dredd, at his side attorneys for the Defense and the Prosecution: Hershey and McGruder. Fargo presides from the highest seat on the dais.

MCGRUDER: "Before we go on, I wish to make a personal comment." (turning) "Judge Dredd. I have observed your career from its outset and I have the highest regard for you. Nevertheless, I must prosecute you to the best of my ability."

DREDD: "That is the law, Judge McGruder. I would expect no less."

FARGO: "The Court shares in Judge McGruder's sentiments. Proceed, Judge McGruder."

Silence around the hall.

MCGRUDER: "The video you have just seen is prima-facie evidence that the defendant is guilty as charged. Mark it People's Exhibit A."

Hershey steps forward.

HERSHEY: "Objection, Your Honor. This video is inadmissible as evidence. If I can be given a moment to explain."

Everyone is surprised.

FARGO: (beat) "Please do."

HERSHEY: "Your Honor, I have here an affidavit from Cadet Olmeyer, currently a Junior at the Academy."

The heads of the other cadets around him swivel to stare at Olmeyer in the audience. He does his best to look cool.

HERSHEY: "Cadet Olmeyer is acknowledged by all his instructors to be an expert in the field of still and video graphics. Top of his class five years running in Computer Programming and Manipulation. Honors four times over. Hall of Justice Certificate of Junior Law. He also helped create and develop Central's video analysis system. His affidavit states that this surveillance video is of such low definition that even after all known enhancements are used, no positive identification can be made."

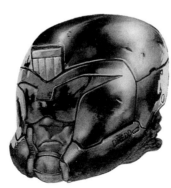

Left: The third version of the Street Judge's helmet, drawn by Simon Murton.

Below left: Two earlier versions of the Street Judge's helmet.

Below: The final version of the Street Judge's uniform.

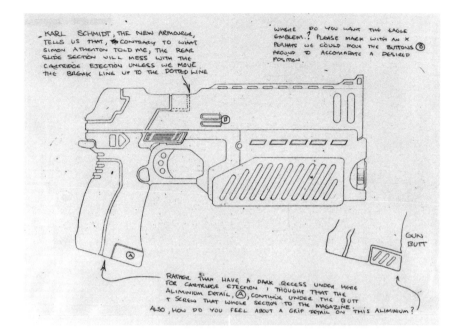

KARL SCHMIDT, THE NEW ARMOURER, TELLS US THAT, CONTRARY TO WHAT SIMON ATHERTON TOLD ME, THE REAR SLIDE SECTION WILL MESS WITH THE CARTRIDGE EJECTION UNLESS WE MOVE THE BREAK LINE UP TO THE DOTTED LINE

WHERE DO YOU WANT THE EAGLE EMBLEM? PLEASE MARK WITH AN X PERHAPS WE COULD MOVE THE BUTTONS (B) AROUND TO ACCOMARATE A DESIRED POSITION.

GUN BUTT

RATHER THAN HAVE A DARK RECESS UNDER HERE FOR CARTRIDGE EJECTION I THOUGHT THAT THE ALIMINIUM DETAIL, (A), CONTINUE UNDER THE BUTT + SCREW THAT WHOLE SECTION TO THE MAGAZINE. ALSO, HOW DO YOU FEEL ABOUT A GRIP DETAIL ON THIS ALIMINIUM?

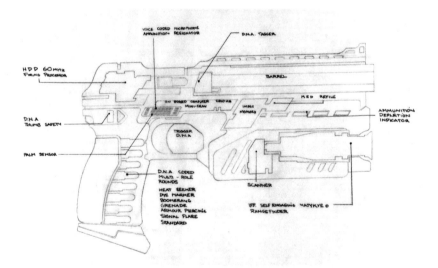

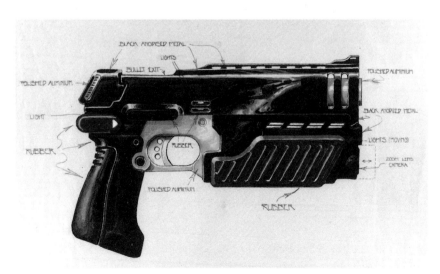

She looks at McGruder, then at the audience.

HERSHEY: "Since the uniform of a Judge could be counterfeit, since the badge could be duplicated, and since neither video nor audio in this clip can identify positively the accused in any way, I repeat my objection to this video being entered as evidence in this case!" (she turns to Griffin) "And I ask for a ruling."

Esposito and Silver look puzzled. Griffin is fixed on Dredd. You could hear a pin drop in the vast room. Everyone watching is sure they know what Fargo will say. They're all wrong. He looks to McGruder and then straight at Dredd.

FARGO: "Objection . . . sustained. The video is inadmissible."

The audience goes nuts. Fargo bangs his gavel.

OLMEYER: "Yesss!"

Hershey returns to stand near Dredd as the court quiets down. Olmeyer whoops a second longer than everyone else. Embarrassed, he quiets down, but not before Dredd notices him.

DREDD: (whispering) "That kid barely knows me and he wants to save my ass."

HERSHEY: (also whispering) "Trust me. It's not your ass he's interested in."

MCGRUDER: "Very well. I'm therefore forced to move to technical evidence of a critical nature." (turning to Hershey) "I will need the Court's permission to access top-secret documentation with the help of Central Computer Bank."

Hershey and Dredd look at each other: Hershey's face drops a mile, as does Olmeyer's. It's not over. Griffin leans over and whispers to Fargo, the pressure starting to show on his face.

FARGO: "You may proceed."

MCGRUDER: "Central? Are you on line?"

A calm voice is heard throughout the large hall.

CENTRAL: "On line, Judge McGruder."

MCGRUDER: "I wish you to access weapons

schematics. Please describe the working of the standard Judge's sidearm, the Lawgiver Two, and especially its improvements over the earlier Lawgiver One."

Somehow Central's monotonous, sexless voice hints at an actual personality.

CENTRAL: "One moment."

On the screen, computer graphics appear illustrating these words.

CENTRAL: "Seven years ago, the Lawgiver Model Two replaced the Model One. The difference lies in two areas: the computer chip and the ammunition coding. Like the Model One, the computer chip recognizes the palm print of its owner: an impostor's hand print will activate the weapon's alarm."

Animation reminds us of this in non-gory fashion.

CENTRAL: "Model Two is coded to the personal DNA of the Judge using the weapon, via the skin's contact with the grip. A fail-safe security precaution."

HERSHEY: (to Dredd) "Did you know about this?"

DREDD: "No."

CENTRAL: "The DNA is obtained from my medical files and upgraded automatically every time the weapon is reloaded. Each time a round is chambered and fired, the projectile is tagged with that relevant DNA."

HERSHEY: "Chief Justice, the defense was unaware of this. As was everybody else here."

FARGO: "Judge Hershey, the prosecution must be given time to finish."

MCGRUDER: "Central. Were the bullets recovered from the bodies of Vardis and Lily Hammond so DNA coded?"

CENTRAL: "Yes, Judge McGruder. It could not be otherwise."

MCGRUDER: "And what was the result of the computer check of the DNA coding on those bullets?"

You could swear that the computer is going for drama. On the screen, a string of DNA appears. A second strand appears next to it. The two slide over each other. They're a perfect match.

CENTRAL: "The DNA is a perfect match for Judge Joseph Dredd."

Above: *The final version of the Lawgiver One by Julian Caldow.*

Opposite top: *A note on an intermediate diagram of the Lawgiver casing suggests an adjustment to avoid the sliding movement of the chamber by Julian Caldow.*

Opposite middle: *A sketch for the design of the newer, fancier Lawgiver Two, which plays a crucial role in the plot of* Judge Dredd *because it is DNA coded to respond only to its official owner, by Julian Caldow.*

Opposite bottom: *Among the "textures" added to this early version of the Lawgiver Two is the reflected image of a typical Mega-City "perp" by Kevin Walker.*

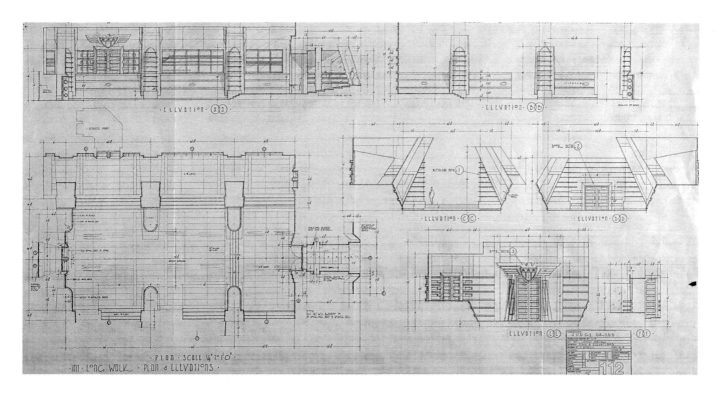

Above: *An architectural elevation of the setting for the Long Walk ceremony by Peter Russell.*

Pandemonium in the Council Chamber. Fargo looks at Dredd as his mind races. Their eyes lock. Fargo has lost confidence in Dredd and lowers his eyes, his head in his hands.

Dredd loses his cool.

DREDD: "It's a lie! This is a setup. It's not possible!"

HERSHEY: (in shock, to Dredd) "DNA evidence is irrefutable! We have no case."

Griffin bangs the gavel.

DREDD: "I wasn't there." (to Hershey) "You believe me, don't you?"

Hershey looks at him, uncertain.

MCGRUDER: "Your Honor, the Prosecution rests."

Griffin looks at McGruder, then toward Fargo, who seems lost.

GRIFFIN: (taking control) "The Tribunal needs to confer."

INT. JUSTICES' CHAMBER CORRIDOR – DAY

An ashen Fargo sits with his face in his hands. Griffin stands nearby, trying to comfort him. Two men alone, moments to decide the fate of a nation.

FARGO: "What have I done? How could I have been so wrong about Dredd. Both of them, homicidal. Only this time, it'll be impossible to cover up."

GRIFFIN: "Chief Justice, we carefully buried the Janus project nine years ago, along with Rico and all his victims. No one will ever learn of your involvement."

FARGO: "The media knows how close I am to Dredd. They'll dig until the whole truth comes out. It's the perfect excuse to ruin what government we have left."

GRIFFIN: "Your motives were pure. You thought Dredd was different. That's why you spared him."

FARGO: "A mistake which may bring down the judicial system."

They contemplate the horrible possibility.

GRIFFIN: "There is a way out, Chief Justice, if you'll forgive me . . ." (beat) "The Long Walk."

Fargo looks at Griffin, indignant.

FARGO: "That's a death sentence, Judge Griffin. Mine."

GRIFFIN: "As Chief Justice, your retirement grants you the power to save Dredd's life."

Fargo looks closely at Griffin. He's right.

GRIFFIN: "This gesture may also allow Janus to remain a secret."

INT. COUNCIL CHAMBER – NIGHT

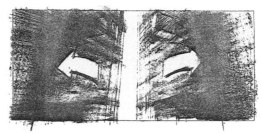

The Foreman of the Tribunal, Council Judge Esposito, stands.

ESPOSITO: "In the charge of Pre-meditated Murder, we find Joseph Dredd guilty as charged."

Gasps from the audience. This is the fall of a legend. Fargo looks Dredd in the eye, hiding a profound sadness. Dredd looks back, unblinking but deeply shaken.

FARGO: "Joseph Dredd, the Law allows only one punishment for your crime. Death."

Shock rebounds from every wall.

FARGO: "However. It has long been our custom to carry out the last order of a retiring Senior Judge."

He pauses. This hurts. He stands.

FARGO: "And so I step down."

On the stand, Dredd is shocked at this news.

DREDD: (under his breath) "No."

FARGO: "As I leave to take my Long Walk into the Cursed Earth, I ask that this Court honor my last order: be lenient with Judge Dredd, in gratitude for his years of service."

Fargo averts his eyes from Dredd and relinquishes his seat to Griffin. Griffin sits down and for a moment luxuriates in the feel of the Chief Justice's seat. Then he picks up the gavel and looks down solemnly at the court and Dredd.

GRIFFIN: (writing this down) "We will so honor this one, Justice Fargo. The sentence shall be, Life Imprisonment in the Aspen Penal Colony."

Dredd looks at Hershey, who is aghast.

GRIFFIN: "Sentence to be carried out immediately.

Above: *Emma Porteous's version
of Fargo's Long Walk outfit.*

Right: *A second architectural
elevation of the setting for the
Long Walk ceremony by
Nigel Phelps.*

As it is written."

*Fargo exits the courtroom alone. Dredd watches.
At the last moment, Fargo turns to look at him, all
faith lost. A sad moment.*
  The Judge Hunters are already coming for Dredd.

HERSHEY: "Griffin! This trial is a farce! I
demand an appeal!"

GRIFFIN: (hard) "You will accept the Council's
decision, and you will accept it without question,
Judge Hershey!"

DREDD: (to Hershey, as he takes her hand) "I
didn't do it. Do you believe me?"

HERSHEY: "Dredd. I'm sorry."

DREDD: "You do believe me?"

HERSHEY: "I believe you."

Griffin reads from the Book of the Law.

GRIFFIN'S VOICE: "Let the Betrayer of the

Law be taken from our Courts."

*The Hunters pull at Dredd. Hershey hangs on as
long as she can.*

HERSHEY: "Dredd . . ."

*Dredd tries to remain calm as he is led away. His
eyes do their best to forgive her.*

GRIFFIN'S VOICE: "Let the Freedom he stole
from others be stolen from himself."

*Dredd stands with wrists manacled, head down. The
Judge Hunters pull off his armor, then literally rip
away his uniform. He's naked, helpless.*

GRIFFIN'S VOICE: "Let his armor be taken from
him, and all his garb of Justice."

INT. WALL – GATES OF MEGA-CITY – SUNRISE

*The ceremony of the Long Walk. Fargo stands alone,
in a long duster coat and a wide-brimmed hat. He
holds his uniform, Lawgiver, and badge in a cere-
monial bundle. The great city gate begins to open.*

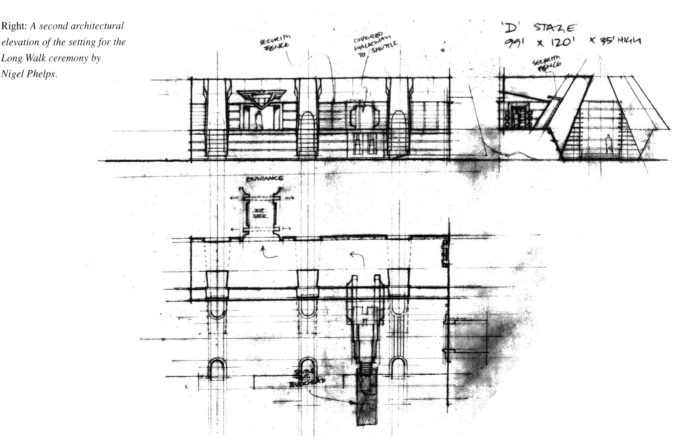

Left: *The explosive Judge pump, built over the stripped chassis of an actual Remington.*

Below: *The gate Fargo walks through on his way into the Cursed Earth, with a dominating eagle motif.*

Under a fading sunset we see the forbidden land beyond: THE CURSED EARTH.

A young female cadet in a sweet contralto that contrasts with Griffin's bass reads from a different part of the Law. Like so many, she reveres this man and what he represents.

FEMALE CADET: "Let him be written in our hearts and our memories."

She hands him the book and receives his bundle of worldly belongings in return. A young male cadet steps forward, hands Fargo an ancient 12-gauge Remington 870 pump shotgun, a relic of a police force long since dead.

INT. WALL – CORRIDOR

With thirty other prisoners – being led to the prison shuttle – all in chains. The others accept their fate. Dredd is still devastated.

GRIFFIN'S VOICE: "Let him be stricken from our hearts and our memories."

A line of cadets raise Lawgivers overhead. Fargo walks through the arch of weapons.

FEMALE CADET: "Forever."

INT. CITY WALL/LOCK – SUNRISE

The doors of the shuttle close. Its engines roar. It leaves the docking bay.

GRIFFIN'S VOICE: "Forever."

EXT. MEGA-CITY ONE WALL – SUNRISE

Fargo stands outside the massive wall. The gate shuts behind him. The shuttle flies away past him. The end of an era.

Above: *The exterior view of Chief Justice Griffin's apartment, rendered here by Matt Codd, was never seen in the finished film.*

Right: *An interior view of Griffin's office that suggests* The Fountainhead, *again by Matt Codd.*

Right: *Six panels from a storyboard sequence by Kevin Walker. Griffin is looking out his window, hears a noise, turns to see Rico sitting in the dark, and rouses the ABC robot.*

INT. GRIFFIN'S APARTMENT – SUNRISE

Griffin comes inside. The flickering firelight casts the huge silhouette of someone sitting in the center of the room. Steam rises from this figure as it slowly stands. As Griffin turns on the lights, he sees the ABC robot looking back at him.

RICO: "Chief Justice Griffin. It has a pleasant ring."

Griffin angrily starts forward, but stops when the robot blocks his path. Its head cranes down to peer into Griffin's face. It growls, like a Tyrannosaurus with a toothache.

GRIFFIN: "We were supposed to meet someplace safe."

RICO: "I like to do things my way. Anyway, this is safe. The reporter is dead. Fargo is on the Long Walk. Dredd is on his way to Aspen."

GRIFFIN: "It's unfortunate. I could've used Dredd. He practically worshiped the ground I walked on."

RICO: "Dredd worships the Law and he'll blow you away the minute he finds out you've been pissing on it. You trust me and let him freeze his ass off in Aspen. Let him see what it's like to be me! After all . . ."

He moves closer to Griffin, smiles.

RICO: "He and I have so much else in common. Why not Aspen?"

Griffin looks at him, and then at the robot, whose eyes burn into him. He decides to drop the subject.

GRIFFIN: "There's a lot of work to be done."

RICO: (pleased) "Janus."

GRIFFIN: "You'll see it soon enough. In the meantime I want chaos. That block war was just the beginning. Now I want fear racing down every street. Then the Council will turn to me. And to Janus."

Rico smiles and moves to the window, looking out at the waking chaos of Mega-City One.

RICO: "Fear. Terror. Panic." (pause) "I think I can handle that."

The proposed set for Chief Justice Griffin's office went through several permutations before it was scrapped. Many of the design elements and furnishings were later moved to the Griffin's apartment set. The quasi-Moorish filigree of the panel behind the desk is a visual motif that appears in several other Dredd *sequences.*

Opposite: *Rico and the ABC robot painted by Kevin Walker.*

Left: *A preproduction conceptual drawing of the prison shuttle by Kevin Walker, with a figure added for scale.*

Below: *Two early designs for prisoners' uniforms by Julian Caldow.*

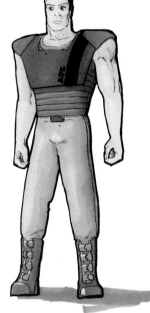

EXT. CURSED EARTH – DAY

A howling wind blows dust across the dead landscape. The Aspen Prison shuttle appears over the horizon.

INT. ASPEN SHUTTLE

A wide cabin with all the amenities of a Roman slave galley. Armed guards patrol the rows of prisoners. Dredd sits stone-faced. The prisoner sitting beside Dredd turns out to be Fergie. He stares at Dredd. There's something about him . . .

Fergie boldly puts his hands over Dredd's face, leaving a gap between his fingers to match the visor slit in a Judge's helmet. It's him, alright.

FERGIE: "Dredd . . ."

DREDD: "What?"

FERGIE: "Don't hit me! What are you doing here?"

DREDD: "I was convicted of a crime. Wrongly convicted."

FERGIE: "That makes two of us."

Behind them a mean-looking prisoner has overheard the name Dredd.

DREDD: "No. You got the sentence the Law required."

FERGIE: "Five years just for saving my own ass? It was a mistake!"

DREDD: "The Law does not make mistakes."

FERGIE: "Oh, yeah? Then how do you explain what happened to you?"

The mean-looking prisoner stares at Dredd's profile. Holds up his hands to match the slit in a Judge's visor . . .

DREDD: "I can't."

FERGIE: (sarcastic) "Oh, you can't. But the Law doesn't make mistakes. So what's this? A bug? A glitch? A typo? A fumble? A screw-up? Or maybe poetic justice?"

EXT. – THE CURSED EARTH – DAY

Four men, Cursed Earth scavengers, watch the shuttle approaching from the horizon. They are the Angel Family, their dustcoats flapping in the outback wind like Sergio Leone's worst nightmare.

JUNIOR ANGEL: "Shuttle coming, Pa."

His father, the Reverend Angel, looks skyward, unfolds his arms. Strange religious tattoos cover his body. His eyes gleam with fanatical energy.

PA ANGEL: "Praise the Lord who brings us this generous bounty." (pause) "My sons, gather the harvest."

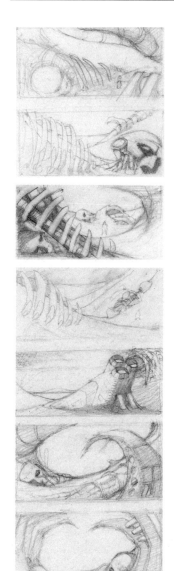

Above: *Various sketches for the Cursed Earth landscape by Chris Halls.*

Right: *The Cursed Earth, showing the top of the canyon by Matt Codd.*

*The Cursed Earth landscape with the
remains of the Capitol Building,
Washington D.C. in the background.*

In this rendition, the Capitol Building has been replaced by a heap of futuristic junk.

INT. SHUTTLE – THE CAGE

The mean-looking prisoner shuffles his hands within their restraints to reveal that he is concealing a small but lethal blade: he looks to his partner next to him. It seems the word is spreading.

BELOW – THE ANGEL BOYS

Pa, Link, and Mean Machine Angel watch proudly as young Junior stands and places a beaten-up, old-fashioned bazooka contraption on his shoulder. A mechanical arm activates a time-bomb.

JUNIOR: "Whoa! Gonna catch me some city boys!"

Junior fires. The rocket shoots up towards the shuttle.
    The magnetic bomb clamps onto the hull of the shuttle. Its red light flashes.

INT. SHUTTLE – THE CAGE
– SAME TIME

The mean-looking prisoner cuts through his restraints. The man next to him smiles to see his comrade free himself. The guards are not looking in their direction.
    The prisoner goes to grab Dredd from behind. Fergie looks up.

FERGIE: "Dredd!"

The prisoner lifts the blade.

PRISONER: "Payback time, lawman!"

Dredd reacts, grabbing the sharp knife next to his throat.

EXT. SHUTTLE

The mechanical bomb's light blinks faster and faster – then goes out.

INT. SHUTTLE

The blade touches Dredd's skin as – KABOOM! – the back of the cabin explodes.

ON THE GROUND

The Angel gang tense with anticipation.

LINK: "She's gonna go!"

PA ANGEL: "C'mon, come to Papa."

INT. SHUTTLE

The explosion rocks the entire craft! It keels over as alarms ring. The mean prisoner is thrown backwards as the pressure is violently sucked out of the cabin. The back section of the shuttle is torn away. A guard fall back, his gun goes off, spewing bullets all over the cabin. One hits one of the pilots, who slumps.

ON THE GROUND

The Angel gang feels the blast. The boys whoop and laugh.

PA ANGEL: "Hallelujah!"

INT. – SHUTTLE

Dredd watches as the uninjured pilot fights to control the seriously damaged craft – his face betraying fear. Fergie screams as they grab on to their seats. The shuttle shakes, the noise deafening. Dredd watches as the fire from the explosion spreads across the ceiling towards the fuel tank. Fergie's eyes widen.

DREDD: (to Fergie) "Hold on! We're going down."

FERGIE: "No shit!"

EXT. SHUTTLE

A fiery explosion as the shuttle is blown into three pieces. The center section shoots out towards camera.

ON THE GROUND

The Angel family watches the crash.

PA ANGEL: "Fine work, sons."

JUNIOR: "Thank you, Pa."

PA ANGEL: (gently chiding) "No, thank the Lord."

ALL: "Amen."

The forward half of the shuttle smashes into the sand, skidding and sliding into rocks, where it finally comes to rest. There's one last groan of metal from the cabin, and then – silence.

INT. JUDGES' LOCKER ROOM – EVENING

Late at night. Hershey slips in. She looks casual at first but her alert manner when she sees two Judges going off shift in the background tells us she has an ulterior motive.

She approaches Dredd's locker. She takes out a jimmy and starts to work on the lock. She hears someone approaching. She starts to hide what she's doing – relaxes with ironic amusement when she sees it's only a cadet cleaning the floor. She returns to what she's doing. The locker clicks open.

She rummages inside. Finds towels, a spare helmet, other routine items. Then an old leather-bound book: "Emerson's Essays". Then a can of brass polish. And another can of brass polish. With a sigh she moves to the bottom shelf . . . and finds boot polish! She can't help but smile. Then she finds a valor award that's been tucked out of sight so long it's covered with dust.

She's about to give up when way in the back she finds a small slipcase. That looks interesting. She rises, moves into the light, and slips out the contents.

It's a framed "viewie". It shows a young couple with a baby.

HERSHEY: "Well. Baby Dredd. Didn't think you were ever a baby."

At her touch, the viewie is illuminated.

She's about to return it to the locker when something about its weight in her hand makes her suspicious. She turns it over to examine it and spots a hidden seal. The frame clicks open.

Inside is a second viewie: Dredd, mid-twenties, with a man we recognize as Rico, who looks about the same age. Both wear cadet uniforms and big grins: it's graduation day at the Academy.

Hershey's puzzled. She has no idea who Rico is. Then a sound of voices makes her look up. It's the next shift of Judges coming into the locker room.

She draws out of sight, pockets the viewie, and exits.

EXT. CURSED EARTH – EVENING

The wreck of the prison shuttle has been surrounded by Judge Hunters. They move through the ruins using bar code readers to scan the ID tags of the dead. Tags attached to their weapons show readings. Another Hunter steps inside through a jagged hole in the fuselage.

SECOND HUNTER: "Sir. We found tracks leading away from the wreck. At least half a dozen people."

The Hunter Squad Leader taps his helmet mike.

HUNTER SQUAD LEADER: "This is Capture Team. No sign of Dredd. He appears to have survived the crash. Repeat, he appears to have survived."

INT. GRIFFIN'S APARTMENT – NIGHT

GRIFFIN: (speaking into an intercom) "You are in error, Capture Team. Dredd did not survive the shuttle wreck. No one survived. Do I make myself clear?"

SQUAD LEADER'S VOICE: "Yessir. Quite Clear."

INT. WRECKED SHUTTLE – NIGHT

ANOTHER HUNTER: "Sir! We found someone."

The Hunters' flashlights converge on an injured guard, the one Dredd saved from the convicts.

INJURED GUARD: "Thank God . . . thank–"

His eyes widen as the Hunters' guns converge on his head. BLAM!

Left: *A rough scetch of the shuttle crash site by Martin Laing.*

Below left: *A drawing to show how the Icelandic landscape should be dressed for the shuttle crash site.*

Bottom: *A painting of the shuttle crash site by Julian Caldow.*

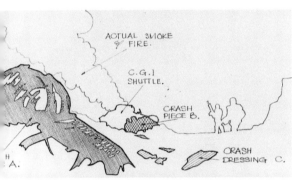

INT. HERSHEY'S APARTMENT – NIGHT

Personal items tell us she's both a danger-crazed athlete and a romantic. Hershey's in sleepwear, her uniform for tomorrow already laid out. She sips coffee from an Academy mug, sits down at her apartment's Central Station.

HERSHEY: "Central, I need to access the graphics database."

Hershey opens the framed viewies she took from Dredd's apartment, removes the one with the adult Dredd, slides it into the computer. The image appears on the screen.

HERSHEY: "I want you to ID this man."

CENTRAL: "Even from here, I can see it's Judge Dredd."

HERSHEY: (exasperated) "The other man!"

CENTRAL: (all business now) "Scanning for identity, unknown, male, approximately 20 Cm tall, weighing ninety-five kilos, Skin Tone Three. Ten. Nine. Eight. Seven. Six."

Suddenly the console goes dead with a beep. The photo image is replaced by the Judge emblem.

HERSHEY: "Central? Central? Hello?"

A CANNED VOICE: (not Central) "This terminal has been disconnected from the main system for a system check. You no longer have access to the system. Thank you."

The viewie pops out of the slot with a thunk. Hershey eyes the computer suspiciously.

INT. DARK CORRIDOR – NIGHT

Griffin and Rico, followed by the ABC robot, walk along what appears to be a dark and dingy steel-structured corridor. Griffin activates a switch, similar to that used by Miller in the high-security cell.

A pneumatic door opens to reveal a large circular room, partially covered and dusty. Rico and Griffin look around, pleased.

GRIFFIN: "Welcome to Janus."

Rico's eyes narrow as he sees a figure move into the light from the shadows: ILSA HAYDEN. A gorgeous but strange-looking woman in her mid-thirties, she projects a cold intelligence with a hint of deeply buried sexuality.

GRIFFIN: (to Rico) "Ah, Rico. I think you know Doctor Hayden?"

RICO: (carefully) "Yes. She's the bitch who testified before the Council that I was insane, and therefore,

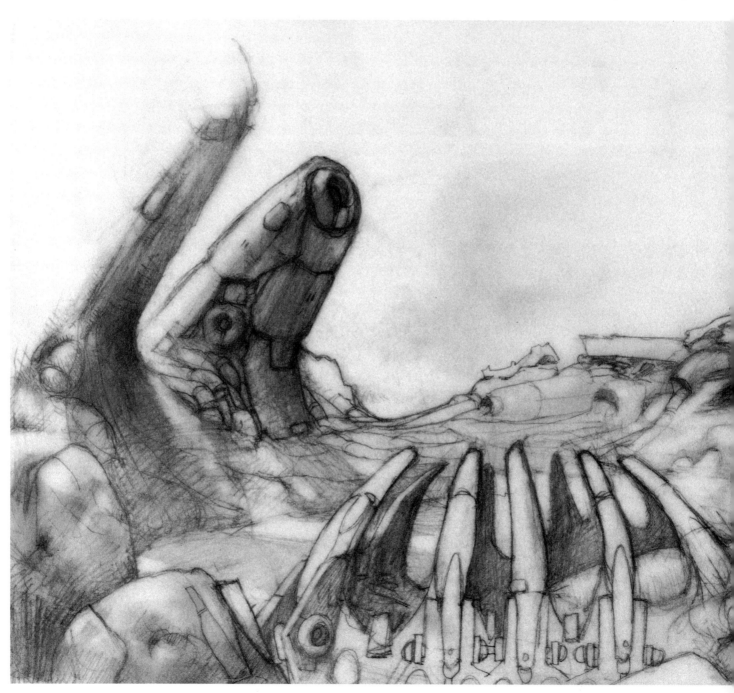

innocent."

ILSA: "I was trying to help you."

RICO: "What you did was insult me. I knew exactly what I was doing. Then and now."

ILSA: "Really?"

Their eye contact is electric. Griffin smiles. Ilsa is not only going to keep an eye on Rico, she is almost

like a gift.

GRIFFIN: "Miss Hayden has been a loyal supporter of this project for a long time: she's kept it alive for me. I'm sure you'll find her . . . expertise invaluable."

ILSA: (looking at the dark machinery) "It won't be up and running without a complete retrofit."

She thrusts a computerized memo pad into Rico's hands. He's annoyed until he sees how accurate it is. Then he's dismayed.

RICO: (reading) "Inducers, nitrogen coils, nano-pumps. Hell, why don't we just nuke the place and start over?"

GRIFFIN: "There's a middle course, I think. I can pull all this from Mega-City hospital. They won't even know it's gone. When can you be on line?"

RICO: "If you really can get these things, tomorrow–"

ILSA: "Tomorrow, provided these items are–"

Rico and Ilsa look at each other sharply. It's not clear to us, or them, if they resent each other or are intrigued.

RICO: "But 'on line' won't mean drok if you can't get into Central's Janus files. They're still security locked."

GRIFFIN: "Leave that to me. Meanwhile you have work to do, on the streets. Ilsa will help you."

RICO: "I don't need any help."

ILSA: (to Griffin) "I thought you said he was created here by the finest scientists in Mega-City. A 'bold experiment.' " (dismissive) "He's a petulant child."

GRIFFIN: "Let's not bicker. We're all committed to the same thing. Ending the squalor and inefficiency of our world. And replacing it with a new society. An ordered society."

RICO: "You'll have your New Order, Griffin."

Rico winks at Ilsa, turns, whistles at the robot like it's a dog.

RICO: "C'mon, Fido. Walkies."

INT. CURSED EARTH/RUINED COURTHOUSE
– NIGHT

*Fergie and Dredd are hanging by their handcuffs
from a pole which in turn has been set on the cross-
beams of this ruined building. Fergie is uncon-
scious. Dredd, awakened by the crawl of a moon-
beam over his face, stirs, looks around.*

*He sees two of the Angels nearby, they're going
through gear and equipment scavenged from the
shuttle wreck. A scream is heard and Fergie wakes
up with a start, and reacts to the dramatic shafts of
moonlight raking the courthouse ceiling.*

FERGIE: "Uh, am I dead? I'm dead!" (seeing
Dredd) "And in hell."

PA ANGEL: "Awake. Good." (off the body)

"We're running out of sinners."

*Reverend Angel and his sons come forward and
throw down the body of a shuttle guard they have
just killed.*

FERGIE: "Oh – my – God. Dredd, do something."

*The Angel gang stops. Pa notices the tattoo on Dredd's
arm, the Judge emblem. He can't believe his luck.*

PA ANGEL: "Dredd? Well, now. Can it be the great
man of the Law himself?"

*Dredd stares at him unmoved. Pa laughs and throws
up his arms.*

PA ANGEL: (nonplussed) "Oh, we are blessed

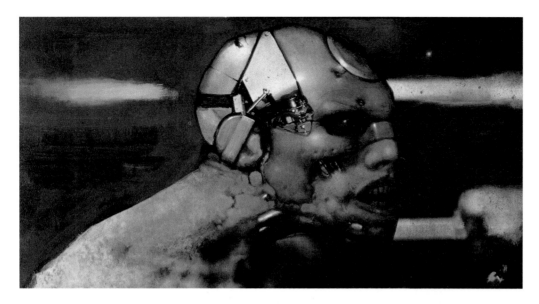

Opposite: The Angel gang painted by Kevin Walker.

Above: Mean Machine by Chris Halls.

indeed, O Lord! All we humbly sought from the craft you guided to us was food and sustenance. But ye have delivered our great enemy into our hands." (in Dredd's face) "Judge Rat Dredd."

DREDD: "You're all under arrest."

MEAN MACHINE: "Is that so! Let me crush him, Pa!"

FERGIE: "We're not together."

They all laugh, except Fergie. Mean Machine steps forward. There is a dial on his head with settings 1–4: mean; surly; vicious; brutal. The Reverend turns the dial to setting 1, mean.

PA ANGEL: "Allow me to introduce you to my family. There's Link."

LINK: "Bite me."

PA ANGEL: "My youngest, Junior."

JUNIOR: "Howdy."

PA ANGEL: "And this here's Mean. Had an accident as a child. The Cursed Earth's a hard place for young folk. I've got him on 1 at the moment, I don't suggest you make him angry. Sorry my youngest son, Fink, can't be here, but then you killed him, didn't you, Dredd?"

DREDD: (controlled anger) "The legendary Angel family. Cursed Earth pirates. Scavengers. Scumbags. Did I miss something?"

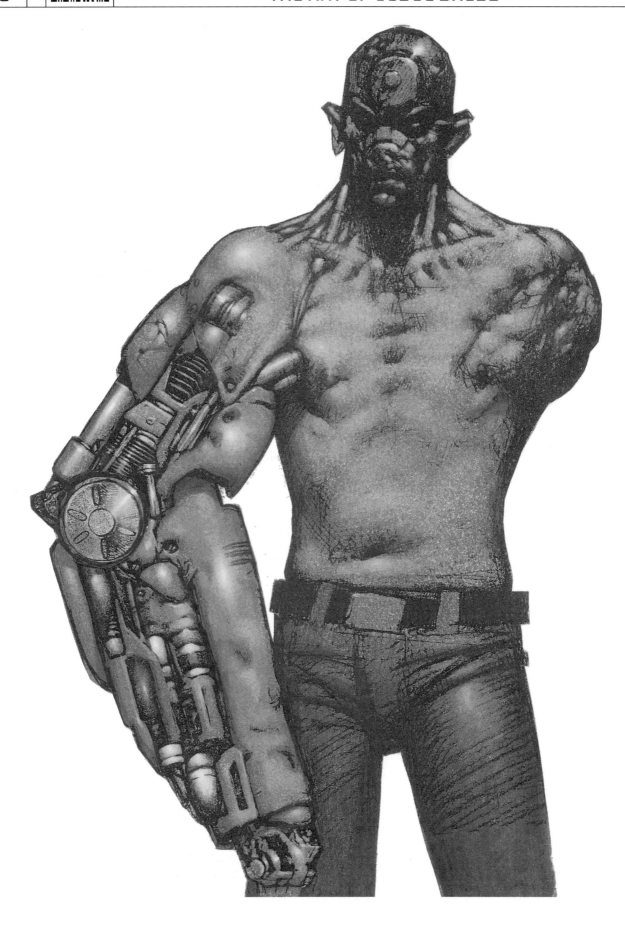

FERGIE: "That'll win them over."

PA ANGEL: "All true, all true. Welcome."

Mean Machine lifts his mechanical arm to Dredd's face. A jagged dagger springs from his wrist. He runs the blade down the front of Dredd's prison shirt, slitting the cloth and drawing blood. The tendons in Dredd's cheeks tense, but he does not cry out.

PA ANGEL: "Sad, though. You still put your faith in a false Law, instead of the one True Law! The Almighty."

Reverend Angel motions to Mean Machine, who cranks his own dial up to 2 (surly) and headbutts Dredd.

JUNIOR: "Let me kill him, Pa. I want his ears."

LINK: "I get the teeth first."

Mean Machine puts a knife to Dredd's tattoo.

MEAN MACHINE: "I want the pretty picture. Then I'll crush him real slow."

FERGIE: (hopeful) "Hallelujah, brother!"

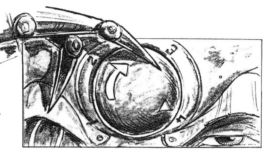

Dredd looks at Fergie suspiciously. Pa Angel looks at him with odd interest.

PA ANGEL: "Wait a second. Can it be? Can it be, that from the City of the Fallen, there is one of the Faithful!"

FERGIE: "Amen, brother! Say it!"

DREDD: "Ah . . . Fergie?"

PA ANGEL: "Boys, I believe we have a Believer in the gallery. Cut him down!"

FERGIE: "Go tell it on the Mountain!"

Fergie smiles as the Angels start to release him.

FERGIE: "Well, Dredd. The Law doesn't make mistakes, but I'm free, and you're toast."

DREDD: "Actually, you're toast. Forgot to mention it. They're also cannibals."

Reverend Angel turns Mean's dial up to 3 (vicious).

Opposite: *Mean Machine by Chris Halls.*

PA ANGEL: "It's been fun, lawman."

The beast slams his metal cranium into Dredd's face.

JUNIOR: "Fresh meat!"

Fergie's expression changes as they cut him down. The Angels' nearby campfire has a spit over it the size of a human being!

LINK: (to Fergie) "You're cute."

PA ANGEL: "Prepare the Supplicant for Sacrifice!"

FERGIE: "Oh, crud! I'm not succulent! I'm not succulent, look, I've got eczema!"

PA ANGEL: "Mean Machine. Finish Dredd."

MEAN MACHINE: "My pleasure."

Mean breaks into a big smile, nods, turns the dial on his own head to 4 (brutal), takes a big swing, and lets the meanest ever headbutt fly.

Like lightning Dredd lifts his whole body weight up. Mean goes flying into the wooden pole behind, cracking his skull wide open.

Dredd and the pole fall to the floor. He throws the ropes off his wrists.

Mean Machine is starting to get to his feet. Dredd slides past him, twisting the dial on his head back down to 1. He continues towards the Angels, who drop Fergie. He scrambles away and the Angels rush Dredd, who doesn't wait for them to reach him. Instead, he charges!

Reverend Angel cranks Mean Machine's dial back up to 4. Mean starts to move just as Dredd sweeps past, twisting the dial back to 1. Mean Machine drops to his knees.

Fergie scampers away, trying to get to the back exit. Junior Angel draws his pistol, but Dredd is too quick, punching him to the floor as he grabs the gun away from him. As Link rushes forward Dredd blasts him with the gun. His dead weight lands on Dredd with a thud.

Reverend Angel raises the metal shaft he has used over his head – turns it point downwards like a spear. Suddenly, BLAM, Reverend Angel is blown backwards.

Judge Hunters pour into the building from all sides, aiming at Dredd, who swings up on the beam again as the wall explodes under him. He pulls himself up onto the wooden balcony and runs, as the floor is chewed up beneath his feet. The balcony breaks.

The Lead Judge Hunter gets right under the balcony. Dredd leaps from it as it collapses. He lands on the waiting Hunter, twisting and cracking his arm, then knocking him down like a Ninja.

Other Judge Hunters charge Dredd. From nowhere, he is up again, taking one Hunter by force, swinging him around so he shoots his partner, then grabbing the Hunter's gun and slamming it into his face.

In hiding, Fergie can't believe it. This man is a killing machine. Fergie goes for the exit, but two Judge Hunters stand above him.

FERGIE: "I surrender! I surrender!"

THIRD JUDGE HUNTER: "Too late."

He aims at Fergie! Dredd is up again and he aims for the Hunters' legs. They fall to the floor. Dredd dives over the rubble and knocks them out.

FERGIE: "Why didn't you kill them?"

DREDD: "Because I'm innocent, remember?"

Calming down from his battle frenzy, he throws down the gun.

FERGIE: (cocky) "Yeah, well, I was ready to jump in, Dredd, but you know, you had it under control."

Behind him, a black figure suddenly moves. Fergie sees it and gets up.

FERGIE: "Dredd!"

Dredd turns. A Hunter is up and aiming at him. The Hunter squeezes the trigger. BLAM! The Hunter himself is hit! A figure silhouetted in the courtroom door fires at the same moment. The Hunter falls, dead. Dredd looks at the new arrival. At his hat. At his long duster coat.

DREDD: "Fargo?"

We see Fargo pleased with himself, his shotgun smoking. His expression suddenly changes to extreme pain as he is lifted off his feet.

SPLORTCH!! Mean Machine runs Fargo through with his mechanical arm. The dial on his head is stuck on four. He lifts Fargo screaming into the air.

Dredd leaps for the Hunter's weapon and blasts Mean Machine, who is wounded and charges into the darkness. Fargo falls on the floor, blood welling on his coat. As he sags, Dredd and Fergie rush forward.

Right: *Max Von Sydow as Fargo in his spaghetti western-inspired Long Walk outfit with his Judge pump drawn by Dermot Power.*

A sketch of the interior of the Cursed Earth courthouse by Nigel Phelps.

Opposite: *Ceiling and gallery plans and elevations of the interior of the Cursed Earth courthouse, drawn by Don Dossett.*

INT. ACADEMY CLASSROOM – NIGHT

Olmeyer is at a graphics work station with his arms folded across his chest. Hershey glares at him.

HERSHEY: "The Dance? You want me to go to the goddamn Junior Dance?"

OLMEYER: "I've given up on the centerfold. I'll settle for a date."

HERSHEY: "We're trying to save Judge Dredd and you're trying to blackmail me?"

OLMEYER: "Yup. I'll never get another chance this good." (looks at console) "It's almost through processing the viewie." (shit-eating grin) "Well? Do we have a deal?"

Her eyes narrow. Instead of what she'd like to tell him, she says:

HERSHEY: (through her teeth) "Yes."

OLMEYER: "Low-cut dress?"

HERSHEY: "Yes! Just do it!"

OLMEYER: (cocky) "Graphics Analysis coming up . . . now."

He hits a control dramatically. The screen displays the picture of Baby Dredd and his parents. Hershey stares at it in disbelief.

HERSHEY: "Olmeyer, you stupid putz! You analyzed the wrong picture!"

OLMEYER: "I did?"

She gropes around on the desk, finds the viewie frame with the shot of Dredd and Rico.

HERSHEY: "This one. You were supposed to do this one! You just wasted three hours! I can't believe it–"

The computer beeps. Messages scroll past.

OLMEYER: "If it's the wrong picture, why is it a fake?"

HERSHEY: "What?"

OLMEYER: "It's full of anomalies. Really clever ones, too. Somebody must have used a CGI terminal and a scan quadrupler to make this. State of the art, twenty years ago."

He looks at the image, uses the mouse.

HERSHEY: "You mean . . . it's not real?"

OLMEYER: "Look. I'll drop out all the artificial pixels."

Hershey's eyes widen in shock as, one by one, the picture elements disappear, dropping down out of the frame scan line by scan line.

OLMEYER: "Sky. Foreground. House. Parents . . . All fake." (turning) "The only thing that's real is the baby."

She's in shock.

INT. CURSED EARTH COURTHOUSE – NIGHT

Fargo lies near the judge's bench. Dredd has dressed his wound and made him as comfortable as possible.

FARGO: "Thirsty."

DREDD: (to Fergie) "Find some water."

Fergie hurries away. Fargo looks up at the Statue of Justice weighing her scales above them.

FARGO: "Ah, the blind lady."

Dredd looks at the strange statue, not understanding.

DREDD: "Who is she?"

FARGO: "Justice. Before your time. She treated everyone the same. No favors. No secrets. The jury was ordinary people. They decided, not us. We should never have taken justice out of their hands."

DREDD: "No, you had to. You brought order to chaos."

FARGO: "Yes, that we did. Solved many problems and created many more."

Dredd looks at him, confused.

FARGO: "I'm dying. This is a good place to do it. Closest thing to a church I know."

He pulls Dredd close. Speaking desperately against the pain.

FARGO: "To be a Judge, Joseph, is perhaps too much power in one person's hands. I once tried to compensate, to create the perfect Judge. We called it Janus."

Dredd looks puzzled.

FARGO: "Four decades ago DNA samples were taken from the original Council members. One was chosen. Mine. We altered it to enhance the best qualities and screen out the worst. Weaknesses. Frailties." (whispers) "We created you."

Dredd stares at Fargo. Stunned.

FARGO: "Yes."

DREDD: "But I had real parents."

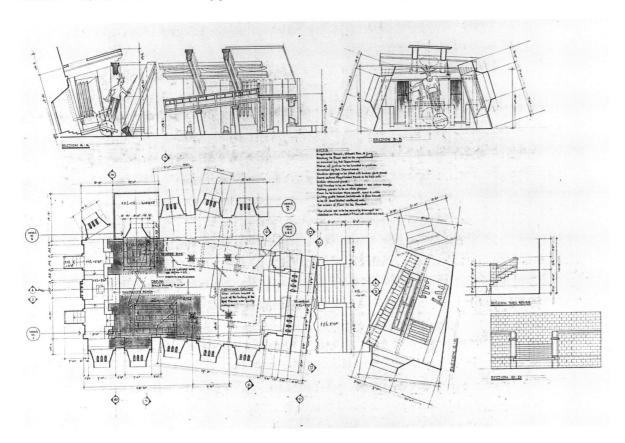

Above: *A painting of the interior of the Cursed Earth courthouse by Matt Codd.*

FARGO: "No."

DREDD: "At the Academy they told me they were killed when I was very young."

FARGO: "A lie."

DREDD: "I have a picture of them."

FARGO: (angry at himself) "A fake! We lied to both of you!!!"

DREDD: "Both?"

mutated into the perfect criminal."

Dredd's mind is reeling.

DREDD: "I have a brother?"

FARGO: "You were best friends at the Academy. Star pupils. Then he turned, and you judged him for his crimes."

DREDD: (accusingly) "Rico? You let me judge my own brother and never told me?!"

FARGO: "I couldn't. You were like a son to me."

DREDD: "A son? My whole life is a lie."

Dredd angrily knocks the cup away. Fargo gazes at him guiltily.

FARGO: "Rico had to be killed. To protect you. To protect the city."

DREDD: "To protect yourself."

Fargo nods weakly, the truth stinging.

FARGO: "Yes. All of us."

Suddenly it hits Dredd. And the realization stuns him.

DREDD: "He's not dead."

FARGO: (shakes his head no) "I signed the order myself. Saw the report."

DREDD: "I didn't kill Hammond. He did it with my weapon and it was his DNA that convicted me. It had to be him!"

Fargo's eyes fill with realization.

FARGO: "Then it was Griffin. We've both been deceived. I'm so sorry, Joseph."

Fargo starts coughing, his death rattle. Dredd cradles him in his arms.

Fargo nods. His strength is ebbing. Fergie rushes back in with a tin cup of water. Dredd quickly lifts it to Fargo's lips. He sips.

DREDD: "Don't die."

FARGO: "Rico's killed me and destroyed you. Find him."

FARGO: "There was another created in the experiment. But something went wrong. Genetically

Fargo dies. Dredd holds him. His eyes fill with anguish.

MEGA-CITY STREET – DAY

A squad of Judges on Lawmasters rides up.

DISPATCHER'S VOICE: (distorted) "All Judges: Report unrest code D-924, downtown sector 12. Back-up requested."

The Judges stop and dismount outside a bank. They enter, careful, and professional. BOOM! The bank explodes, throwing glass, flame, and Judges' bodies into the street.

DOWNTOWN DARK ALLEYWAY – DAY

Six Lawmasters park at the head of the alley. The Judges sweep the alley with batons, clearing away the bums and tramps. The last Judge hears a noise, turns to see some metal shape. The Judges aren't quick enough. They are massacred.

INT. JUDGES' LOCKER ROOM – DAY

Frenzied activity as several shifts double up. A female Judge moves to her locker and is surprised to find it unlocked. Puzzled, she opens it . . .

EXT. HALL OF JUSTICE – DAY

The explosion blossoms against the flank of the great metal eagle.

EXT. DOWNTOWN ALLEYWAY – DAY – CONTINUING

Two of the bums dressed in rags now walk over to the dead Judges who moved them on. They lower their hoods to reveal Rico and Ilsa. Rico smiles proudly at his work.

EXT. MEGA-CITY WALLS – BINOCULAR MATTE – DAY

Dredd peers at the city through binoculars.

FERGIE: "There's no way in!"

Dredd and Fergie are standing beside the Hunters' sand cruiser. Their faces are dry and their lips parched. Dredd has a pack of gear on his back, and Fargo's Remington. Ignoring Fergie, Dredd continues to peer at the Mega-City wall.

FERGIE: "Hey, did you hear me? They don't have

Left: *A Mega-City street scene painted by Simon Murton.*

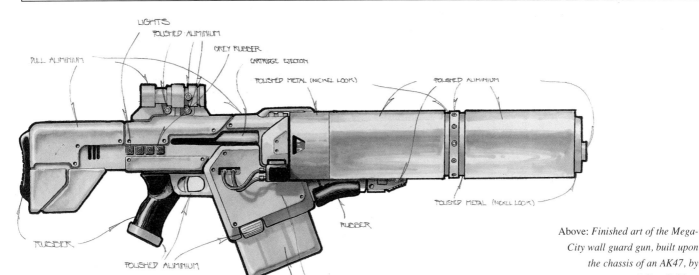

Above: *Finished art of the Mega-City wall guard gun, built upon the chassis of an AK47, by Julian Caldow.*

Left and opposite: *Two designs for the Aspen Prison guard and Mega-City wall guard uniforms by Julian Caldow. The cape is used to differentiate Aspen Prison guards from Mega-City wall guards, otherwise the uniform and the gun are the same.*

Below: *Wall guard helmet designs by Little John.*

a welcome mat!"

DREDD: (lowering binoculars) "There's a way in. Six years ago two Cursed Earthers figured it out."

He points. Sure enough, there's a puff of flame at a vent low on the wall. Smoke rises into the sky. Then it stops.

DREDD: "The vent from the city incinerator."

FERGIE: "And these Cursed Earthers, they made it through?"

DREDD: "Let's go."

FOOM! Another fireball shoots out of the vent. Fergie stares at it, panicking, as Dredd starts forward.

EXT. MEGA-CITY STREET – NIGHT

Sirens wail. Fire burns around the corner. Several Lawmasters cruise past, pursuing looters. Hershey throws two perps against a fence, and cuffs them to it.

HERSHEY: (into radio) "Dispatch, I'm in Green Quad, 4-11. Need pickup."

DISPATCH VOICE: "We copy, Hershey. I have Central on line for you. Can you take it?"

HERSHEY: "Patch it through the Lawmaster."

As she walks to her bike a drone can be heard, and the street lights around her flicker and fade for a second. She frowns, troubled, and mounts the Lawmaster. As she does, she notices something. Her

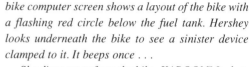
bike computer screen shows a layout of the bike with a flashing red circle below the fuel tank. Hershey looks underneath the bike to see a sinister device clamped to it. It beeps once . . .

She dives away from the bike. KABOOM! It shatters into a thousand flaming pieces.

EXT. INCINERATOR CHUTE – NIGHT

Fergie and Dredd balance on the chute's thin ledge. A fireball rolls toward them. As it disappears into the sky, Dredd and Fergie look at each other, both hearts beating.

DREDD: "Ready?"

FERGIE: (to himself) "No."
DREDD: (annoyed) "What's wrong?"

FERGIE: "What's wrong? Are you kidding? Did wearing that helmet all those years compress your brain? You're gonna get me killed!"

DREDD: "There's a maniac loose in the city."

FERGIE: "There's one loose out there, too! Great time I'm having. The shuttle crash, the Cursed Earth, cannibals and now fireworks up my ass. This is all your fault!"

DREDD: "My fault?"

FERGIE: "Yes! If you hadn't arrested me, I wouldn't be here in the first place."

He sits down petulantly.

FERGIE: "That's it. That's it. I'm through schlepping. I'm gonna sit here until I'm caught. Or until you apologize."

DREDD: "The Law doesn't apologize."

FERGIE: "But that's just it. You're not a Judge any more. So apologize."

DREDD: "What's it matter?"

FERGIE: "Come on. No one's listening. Do it. You've never said those words in your life. Just admit it. You owe it to me."

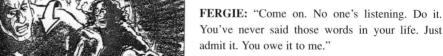

Dredd turns around, whips up the shotgun and points it at Fergie. Then slowly lowers it.

DREDD: "I . . . I'll review your case."

FERGIE: (it'll do) " 'Review' is good. That's better. Almost human, my man." (beat) "We can do it, right?"

DREDD: "Fergie, run!"

Crouched over, they swing into the chute.

INT. CHUTE

They run for their lives.

FERGIE: (as he runs) "Thirty . . . twenty-nine . . . twenty-eight . . . twenty-seven . . . twenty-six . . . twenty-five . . ."

Fergie's already beginning to drop back.

DREDD: "Stop counting!"

FERGIE: (softer) "–nineteen . . . eighteen . . . seventeen . . . sixteen . . ."

Faint light starts to fall on Dredd. Then he sees them up ahead, the lights of Mega-City! He turns to look at Fergie, who's still halfway back.

FERGIE: (panting) "Twelve . . . eleven . . ."

He falls, then tries to get up. His shirt is caught on the conduit! He struggles, in a panic, but keeps counting!

FERGIE: "Ten! Oh God, nine. Dredd! Help me! EIGHT! FOR GOD'S SAKE!"

He looks over his shoulder just in time to see the fireball ignite and start to race towards him.

FERGIE: "Dredd! Don't let me fry."

Dredd turns, lifts the Remington toward Fergie, and racks the slide.

FERGIE: "Uh, on second thought–"

BOOM! Dredd fires down at the grate beneath Fergie's feet. The grate falls away and Fergie hangs there for a beat. Then his own weight rips his sleeve free and he falls down the duct.

   Dredd leaps in after him, as the fireball swirls around him!

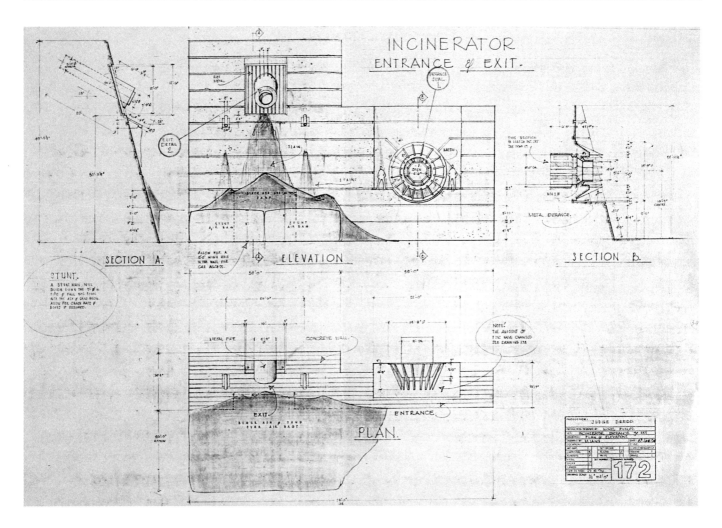

Above: *Plan and elevations of the incinerator entrance and exit, drawn by Martin Laing.*

EXT. WALL IN MEGA-CITY – NIGHT

Fergie is catapulted out of the opening, landing head first in a pile of ashes. He looks around.

FERGIE: "I'm alive. I'm alive! Yes!!"

He turns to see Dredd fall out behind him, also covered in ashes.

FERGIE: "Oh. So are you."

INT. COUNCIL CHAMBER – NIGHT

Chief Justice Griffin, Council Judges McGruder, Esposito and Silver.

ESPOSITO: (stricken) "Latest casualty report, ninety-six Judges have been assassinated."

MCGRUDER: "Whoever's doing it knows all our procedures, our security measures, even out scrambled frequencies."

ESPOSITO: "With no Judges on the street, riots are breaking out all over Mega-City–"

SILVER: "We can't replace those Judges! Even if we put the Cadets on the street we won't be at full strength for years!"

GRIFFIN: "There is a solution." (on their glances) "Project Janus."

MCGRUDER: (furious) "Chief Justice Griffin, just mentioning that is grounds for impeachment."

SILVER: "The Council tried to play God once before. It almost destroyed them."

GRIFFIN: "If this wholesale slaughter of Judges continues, there won't be a Council! Janus could–"

ESPOSITO: "Janus could what! A new batch of test-tube babies won't solve this crisis! We don't need reliable Judges twenty years from now – we need them today!"

GRIFFIN: "Accelerated Growth Incubators are even more developed now. We could create adult subjects, fully grown and fully trained at birth. We could replace the Judges we've lost in a week."

MCGRUDER: "Good God! What are you saying?"

GRIFFIN: "All I'm asking is that we unlock the Janus files. That way, we at least have an option. Please let us find out. If the Council decides not to go forward, I'll accept that decision, and resign."

The Judges look at each other.

INT. LOCKER ROOM – HALL OF JUSTICE – NIGHT

Technical staff are finishing up cleaning the wreckage from the explosion. The leader reports to a Judge. As the Judge leaves, he hears a noise behind the lockers, he stops, moves closer, around a corner. Fergie stands there wearing an uncomfortable grin. He waves. The Judge frowns, then from behind, WHACK! Dredd. Dredd starts to take off his uniform.

    Fergie slides down a locker, lost, no energy left.

FERGIE: (whispering) "Why not? What else can they do to me? I'm dead already."

Dredd looks up at him as he changes, almost smiles.

INT. COUNCIL CHAMBER – NIGHT

Around the great table dais, they give their codes into Central's monitors.

JUDGE MCGRUDER: "McGruder, Evelyne. Council Judge. Authorize access to file, code name Janus."

CENTRAL: "Acknowledged."

On the monitors, graphics show data locks being removed one be one.

JUDGE ESPOSITO: "Esposito, Carlos. Council Judge. Authorize access to file, code name Janus."

CENTRAL: "Acknowledged."

SILVER: "Silver, Gerald. Council Judge. Authorize access to file, code name Janus."

CENTRAL: "I have unanimous authorization for access to file, code name Janus. Removing security blocks now. Awaiting password command from presiding Chief Justice."

Griffin has been waiting for this moment.

GRIFFIN: "Password, origin."

Left: *An early conception of the Council Chamber by Nigel Phelps.*

Above: *An early conception of the Council Chamber by Matt Codd. A lower ceiling was added to make a more grim and menacing mood.*

CENTRAL: "Janus file open."

Griffin smiles. Moves in front of the machine, speaks tersely.

GRIFFIN: "Central, using current technology, how long would it take for Janus to produce a fully grown adult subject?"

CENTRAL: "Given the current state of genetic engineering an adult subject could be incubated in approximately eight hours."

Astonishment in the room.

INT. HALL OF JUSTICE CORRIDOR – NIGHT

Dredd marches Fergie down the Hall corridor. Fergie drags behind and pulls faces. Dredd turns. Fergie drops it. Dredd looks away, and Fergie starts again.

They pass a Judge who slows, then turns, watching them head to the Council Chamber.

INT. COUNCIL CHAMBER

GRIFFIN: "In what quantity?"

CENTRAL: "Laboratory Number One is equipped with a hundred. If fully operational, seven hundred subjects could be produced a week."

SILVER: "My God. We could replace our losses in a day."

MCGRUDER: "Why are we considering this?"

ESPOSITO: "This is inhuman."

GRIFFIN: "No. It is the answer."

ESPOSITO: "It's madness. It is not for this Council to play God."

GRIFFIN: "We sit in judgment over man."

MCGRUDER: "No! Judge Griffin, please restore the security blocks."

INT. HALL OF JUSTICE – CORRIDOR

Dredd gets to the doors, the Council's meeting inside, he can hear voices. The door is locked.

INT. COUNCIL CHAMBER

GRIFFIN: "It seems none of you have the force of will that these times require. Central, leave Janus unlocked."

McGruder stands, furious.

MCGRUDER: "Griffin, this is treason! You just sealed your fate!"

GRIFFIN: "No. I've just sealed yours. Rico!"

Rico steps into the room, an arm-length assault rifle at his waist. He levels it . . .

EXT. COUNCIL CHAMBER – NIGHT

Dredd is about to open the door with a blast from the shotgun when a hand grabs his shoulder and spins him around. It's the Judge who followed him.

JUDGE: "Hey, Dredd! I thought it was you–"

That's all he has time to say before Dredd K.O.s him. He lifts the shotgun again . . .

INT. COUNCIL CHAMBER

MCGRUDER: (in shock) "Rico!"

All the Judges go for their Lawgivers, but it's too

The Judge Hunters' automatic rifle by Julian Caldow.

late. *Rico open fire on full automatic.*

RICO: "Who says politics is boring?"

BOOM! Dredd blasts the door open.

DREDD'S VOICE: "NOOOOOOOO–!"

Rico whirls, confronts Dredd, who screams in fury.

DREDD: "YOU MURDERING SON OF A . . ."

Griffin tries to get off a shot at Dredd, can't. Then Griffin hears alarms, shouts, running footsteps. He steps between the brothers.

GRIFFIN: (to Rico) "No! Get out of here, now!"

Sounds. People running, Rico obeys. He slips out.

DREDD: "Griffin. You're under arrest."

GRIFFIN: "Really?"

For a moment we think he's going to shoot. Then he turns his gun and points it at his own arm, and fires!
    Dredd is totally thrown by the maneuver. He hesitates. Behind him the Judge Hunters rush to see the shocking scene: the wounded Chief Justice clutching at his own bloody arm.

GRIFFIN: "Stop him! He just killed the entire Council!"

Dredd realizes he's fucked. He turns, runs. The Judge Hunters pause near their wounded leader, who bravely waves them on. They tear after Dredd like wolves.   .

INT. HALL OF JUSTICE CORRIDOR – NIGHT

Dredd tears around the corner. Fergie appears from behind the hiding place he ducked into at the first shots!

FERGIE: "Dredd! Tell them I'm innocent!"

Bullets rip up the wall nearby! Dredd drags him along. They crash through doors marked "Academy Classrooms".

INT. ACADEMY TRAINING CENTER – NIGHT

Bullets whiz past Dredd and Fergie's heads. They enter the training center and Dredd runs right towards the Mark IV Lawmaster, leaps into the saddle, kicks over the engine. Fergie holds onto Dredd as the pursuing guards appear. Dredd hits the bike computer and the wheels lift up into the chassis. The engine whirrs.

DREDD: "C'mon, baby, work for me."

The bike splutters, shakes.

FERGIE: "What's wrong with this thing?"

The Judges and guards are gaining, blasting away.
    At the end of the corridor, a wall. No way out.

FERGIE: "Where are you going?!"

Dredd hits the bike cannons. The fenders fold out to reveal high-tech sidearms. The bike moves forward as – BLAM! – a hole is blasted in the wall, revealing Mega-City hundreds of stories below!

FERGIE: "Dredd? Dredd, you're not gonna–"

Dredd hits the button marked "AERIAL MODE". There's a beep and the strained sound we heard ear-

lier when the flying prototype failed.

DREDD: (a prayer) "Please work."

They pick up speed, moving toward the drop. The half-hearted sound of the Aerial Mode lifters isn't encouraging. They just groan.

DREDD: "Pleaseworkpleaseworkpleasework–"

FERGIE: "OhGodohGodohGodohGod–"

They pick up speed. The wall explodes with gunfire around them, as they crash through the irregular hole!

EXT. ACADEMY – NIGHT

Dredd and Fergie fly out of the building on the Lawmaster Mark IV. Barely hanging on, they fall silently through the air, glass spinning all around them. The bike begins to turn a somersault.
    The bike computer's Aerial Mode indicator flashes.

The Wonderful Mega-City of Oz, detailing the three distinct social/economic layers, by Nigel Phelps.

DREDD: "Pleasssssssssse–"

The busy street below rushes towards them.

FERGIE: "We're going to die!"

And then, the flying motorcycle comes out of its roll *with a blast of rockets, and roars upwards!*

INT. ACADEMY TRAINING ROOM – NIGHT

The Judge Hunters react as the bike disappears in an instant, streaking across the sky like a comet. Then, they turn, surprisingly nonplussed!

Dredd and Fergie aboard the cycle. Fergie struggles to stay aboard as Dredd fights to control the Lawmaster.

EXT. ACADEMY – NIGHT

FERGIE: "Dredd! Where's the seat belt!"

DREDD: "Be quiet! I'm still trying to figure this out!"

FERGIE: "I won't even ask about the air bag."

Fergie looks over his shoulder, glad to escape. But his face drops.

An early version of Judge Dredd on a flying Lawmaster by Matt Codd.

To fill out the airborne traffic patterns of Mega-City One, the Dredd art department designed several typical urban vehicles.

From top: SkyVan, Honda Shuttle, U-Freight-Eez Transport, Mini-Container Transport and Greyhound "Canyon" Bus, by Julian Caldow.

Main picture: Fuel barge by Kevin Walker.

The three Judge Hunters zoom from around the back of the building, all on flying bikes. They turn in formation in pursuit.

DREDD: (looking) "Great."

FERGIE: "Oh, shit! Whatta we do? Oh, shit!"

Dredd twists the throttle. Fergie falls from the saddle, holds onto Dredd's belt. All four bikes whiz through the skyline, narrowly missing other traffic and roadworks. Up ahead is a huge video poster. Dredd heads straight for it. Fergie buries his head in Dredd's back.

Dredd looks behind to see them still on his tail, then hands Fergie the shotgun.

DREDD: (shouting over the wind) "Cover our rear!"

FERGIE: (clumsily taking it) "But . . . I never shot a gun in my life."

DREDD: "What the hell kind of criminal are you?"

FERGIE: "A nice criminal."

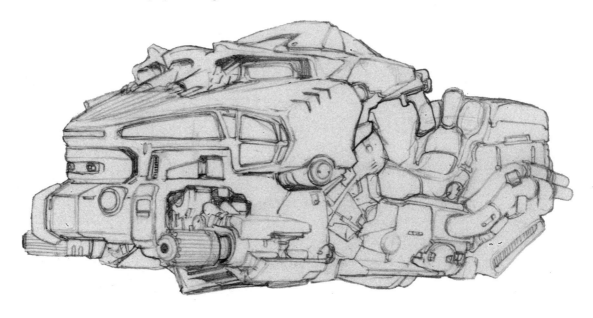

Above: A sketch of a two-seater flying Lawmaster.

Right: An early sketch of a flying Lawmaster.

DREDD: "Shoot!"

Fergie shoots and misses the leading Hunter.

DREDD: "Again."

Fergie pulls the trigger. An empty click.

DREDD: "What happened?"

FERGIE: "The batteries must be dead!"

DREDD: "You have to take off the safety, you moron!"

FERGIE: "Now he tells me . . ."

He struggles with the lever. Click. Then BOOM! BOOM! A hit. Fergie's shot damages the furthest Hunter's bike computer; smoke and sparks fly off.

A video poster is flickering on and off. When it's on, 3-D lasers zap together with force.

Dredd and Fergie go right through the 3-D hologram poster.

Hunter Number One follows. Hunter Number Two turns and twists ninety degrees to the side, shooting under it.

Hunter Number Three can't get the bike to move quickly enough. Its computer reads "damage". He screams as KABOOM! He smashes straight into it as image and laser come together. He's like a fly caught in a very big zapper. The explosion is massive. Dredd and the two remaining bikes fly away from the fireball like shrapnel.

Fergie shrugs, cocky.

FERGIE: "I meant to do that."

BLAM! BLAM! Flak explodes close enough to singe their hair!
    Then they're hit, smoke billows from their bike. Dredd has no choice but to head down.

FERGIE: "Are you crazy, Dredd? There are people down there."

We fly down into a busy Mega-City street, not just

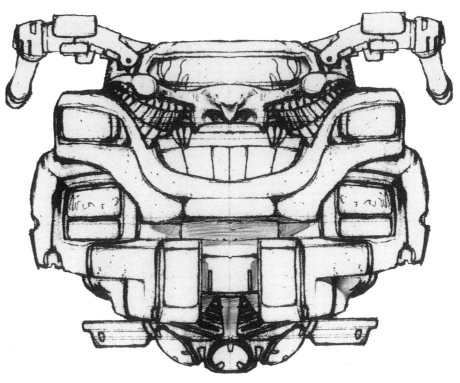

Drawings of a flying Lawmaster by Kevin Walker.

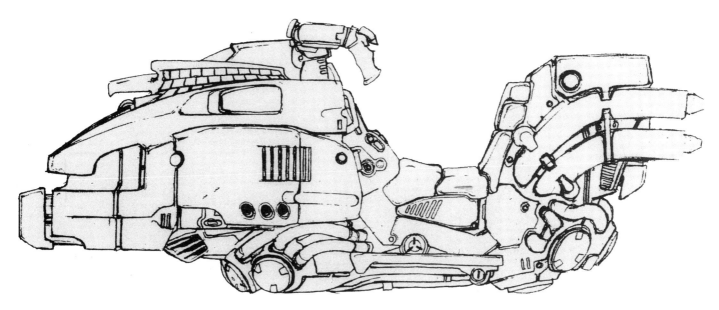

*Matt Codd's view of the
mid-levels of Mega-City.*

An early version of the upper levels of Mega-City by Kevin Walker, with the silhouette of a fuel barge added upper left.

people but rioting people, the chaos in the streets that Rico's slaughter of the Judges has wrought. They scream, scattering as Dredd's cycle whizzes by.

FERGIE: "Hey, I know that guy! Why don't you just drop me off–"

Dredd looks back at him.

FERGIE: "Never mind."

The Judge Hunters land behind them, less sympathetic to the pedestrians. Bike cannons blaring, anyone in the way is toast. Shop windows smash, cars

crash. *Dredd speeds towards the end of the street – and a solid wall.*

FERGIE: "Dredd? Er, Dredd, that's a brick wall."

The Judge Hunters see the dead end. They think they have him. Inches from the wall. Fergie covers his face. Dredd pulls his bike with all his strength.

FERGIE: "A – brick – wall – Noooo!"

With a screech, Dredd swoops straight up the wall.
Hunter Number Two looks up, then back down in time to eat bricks. The bike crashes through the wall.

INT. ELDERLY COUPLE'S APARTMENT – NIGHT

The elderly couple is glued to the visi-screen as the Judge Hunter's bike plows to a stop in the middle of the living room.

ABOVE THE CITY

Hunter Number Three pulls up and keeps shooting. Dredd's bike takes another hit and slows down. Hunter Number One pulls up beside him. There is nothing Dredd can do. The Hunter draws his Lawgiver and aims.

DREDD: "Steer."

FERGIE: "What?"

DREDD: "Steer!"

FERGIE: "But!"

Dredd leaps off, just catching the Hunter's pipework, which is so hot it burns his hands. The Hunter is amazed, having no time to react as Dredd's hand grabs him by the belt and pulls him off. He falls thousands of feet.
Dredd sits up and swerves the Hunter's bike.
Fergie is left on the damaged and smoking bike, heading straight towards a building. He suddenly turns religious, crossing himself furiously. The building speeds toward him. Closer, closer. We can see the brickwork as . . .
Dredd's hand plucks him off the bike from above. The damaged bike smashes into the concrete with an explosion as Dredd on the Hunter's bike pulls the dangling Fergie on board.
Dredd almost manages a smile as Fergie looks back at the fireball from the building.

FERGIE: "Never again. Never driving with you again, you hear me? Never."

The bike shoots off into the moonlit city like a shooting star.

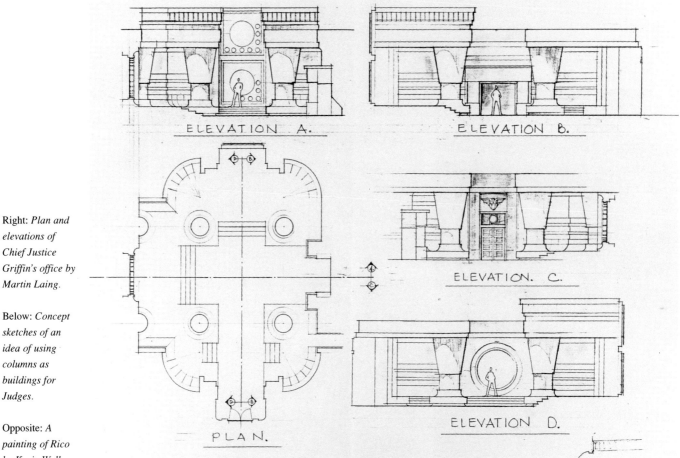

ELEVATION A.

ELEVATION B.

ELEVATION C.

ELEVATION D.

PLAN.

Right: *Plan and elevations of Chief Justice Griffin's office by Martin Laing.*

Below: *Concept sketches of an idea of using columns as buildings for Judges.*

Opposite: *A painting of Rico by Kevin Walker.*

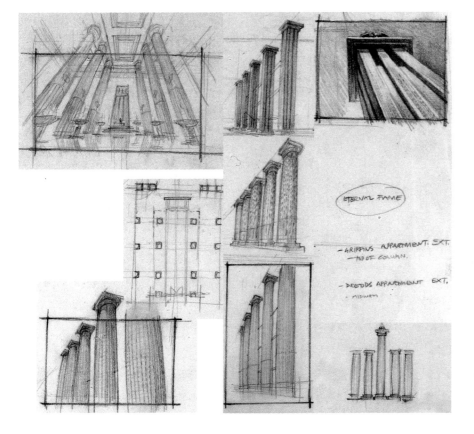

INT. GRIFFIN'S APARTMENT – NIGHT

A medic leaves. Griffin, bandaged, turns as Rico comes out of hiding.

RICO: "Why didn't you let me kill him when I had the chance?"

GRIFFIN: "He'll keep the Street Judges preoccupied while we work on Janus." (turning) "Central. Prepare the Janus Lab for full operation. And while you're at it, I'd like to appoint Judge Rico to the Council of Judges."

CENTRAL: (guarded) "That may present some legal difficulties, since Judge Rico is listed as being executed fifteen years ago."

GRIFFIN: "Your listing is obviously in error."

CENTRAL: "Central does not make errors. Judge Rico must have been executed."

RICO: "I got better."

INT. HERSHEY'S APARTMENT BUILDING – NIGHT

Moving carefully, Dredd and Fergie walk down the corridor. Dredd is still in the stolen uniform.

A nameplate with Hershey's name on it. The door has been forced open. Dredd and Fergie look at each other. Dredd swings the Remington out of hiding, steps inside.

INT. APARTMENT – NIGHT

A total wreck. All the furniture has been overturned, and Hershey's computer has been smashed.

FERGIE: "I guess you're out of friends, Dredd."

Dredd moves into a corridor leading to a bedroom. It is dark.

She is beaten up from the blast, angry and confused.

DREDD: "Hershey, I thought they . . ."

HERSHEY: "Thought they what? Killed me? Thought or hoped?"

DREDD: "What happened?"

HERSHEY: "Why don't you tell me? They're dying out there, Dredd. A hundred and eight Judges in forty-eight hours. What the hell is going on?"

Dredd is lost, exhausted and broken, he doesn't know where to start.

DREDD: "You don't think I'm part of this?"

HERSHEY: "I don't even know who – or what – you are any more."

DREDD: (quietly) "I would never hurt you, Hershey."

She relaxes her hold on him. Throws something down. The viewie picture of Dredd and Rico.

HERSHEY: "So, tell me about him, Dredd. Make me believe in you again the way I did when I defended you."

DREDD: "His name is Rico. He's my brother. He was the best Judge on the street. The smartest, the most dedicated. But he became insane. He said Judges should rule, not serve. He became more dangerous than any criminal. A lot of men died trying to stop him. I had to judge him."

Left: *An early version of a circular theme on Hershey's apartment drawn by Matt Codd.*

Below: *Elevation of center bay in Hershey's apartment by Martyn John.*

FERGIE: "Look, let's get back to hiding in the lower levels where I know how to survive."

Dredd senses something. Then a shape explodes from the shadows. Dredd is thrown against the wall. A gun in his face.

HERSHEY: "You know the drill. Hands against the wall."

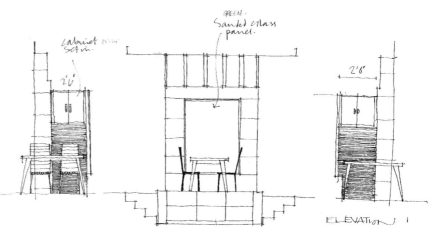

HERSHEY: "And he's doing all of this?"

DREDD: "With Griffin."

HERSHEY: "Griffin? We have to notify the Council."

DREDD: "No. There is no Council, Hershey. They were all murdered an hour ago."

FERGIE: "Perhaps I could fix this terminal and get through to Central."

Hershey has been on her feet for days and this is the last psychic blow. She sags. Dredd catches her.

INT. JANUS LAB – NIGHT

Rico is at the main control console. The robot watches Ilsa closely as she enters.

CENTRAL: "The DNA sample has been taken out of frozen stasis. I am ready to begin the cloning process."

RICO: (to Ilsa) "Slight change of plans, Central. I want to purge that DNA sample."

Ilsa looks up startled as the computer whirrs.

ILSA: "What are you doing?"

He ignores her.

RICO: "Central, activate the DNA sampling console."

Behind Rico, another console lights up. Rico crosses to it.

CENTRAL: "The sampling console is ready."

Rico rips his sleeve open to the elbow and sits down. He puts his upturned arm in a special steel hollow. Clamps close, holding his arm down.

RICO: "Central. Take DNA sample . . . now!"

A drill-like device descends with a frightening grind. And stabs right into his arm!
  Ilsa jumps, startled. A fleck of blood splatters on her clothes.

ILSA: "This wasn't part of our plan. Judge Griffin

never authorized us to–"

RICO: (grabbing her) "Griffin got to be my keeper because he put me behind bars. What's your excuse?"

ILSA: (pulling away) "Griffin is a brilliant man. He's going to turn Mega-City around."

RICO: "Griffin is a file clerk. All he's doing is exploiting my genius. And yours. We're the titans. He's a dwarf."

ILSA: "It was a mistake to keep you alive."

RICO: "I am the future."

ILSA: "You're insane."

He moves in closer to her. She backs up, stopped by the wall of machinery behind her.

RICO: "You didn't believe that. When you said it at my trial." (with a grin) "And you don't believe it now."

She drops her frown and looks deep into his eyes.

RICO: "You're a beautiful woman, Ilsa. Perhaps we should share this moment. Others could do worse than to be created in your image."

He reaches out, touches a drop of his own blood on her sleeve, wipes it on her cheek, then her lips – and she licks the blood, sucking his fingers into her mouth. He pulls her into his arms.

INT. HERSHEY'S APARTMENT – NIGHT

Dredd sits with Hershey on the bed. Both are tired, beaten and bruised. Visible through the door to the living room is Fergie, working on the computer terminal.

HERSHEY: (wryly) "That's why the DNA convicted you. You and Rico are . . ."

Opposite: *A typical computer terminal by Julian Caldow.*

Below: *Elevation of Hershey's apartment by Martin Laing.*

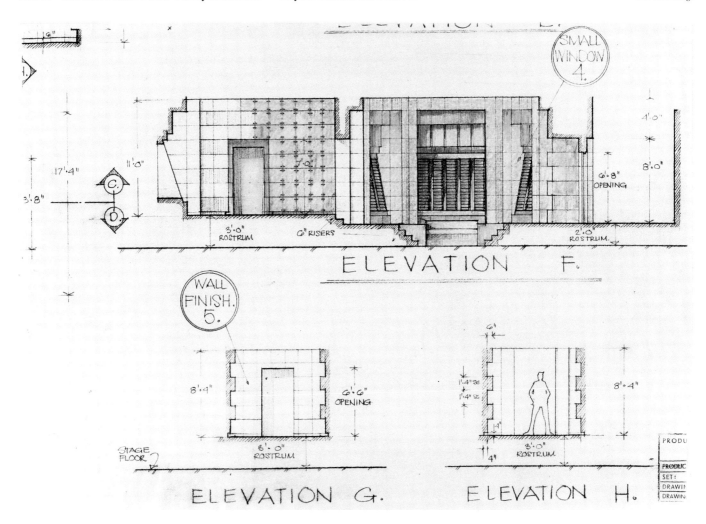

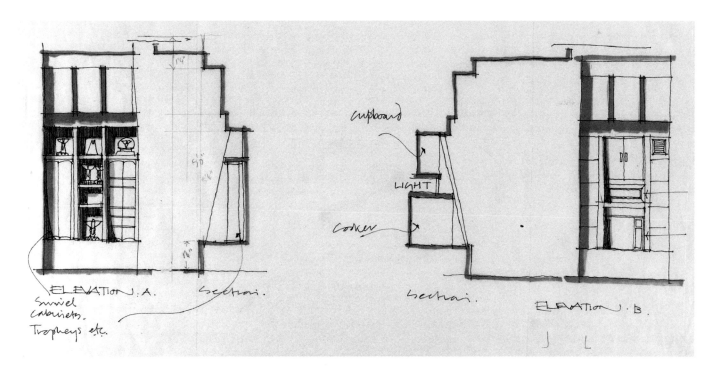

ELEVATION : A.
Swivel
cabinets.
Trophys etc.

Section.

cupboard

LIGHT

cooker

Section.

ELEVATION . B.

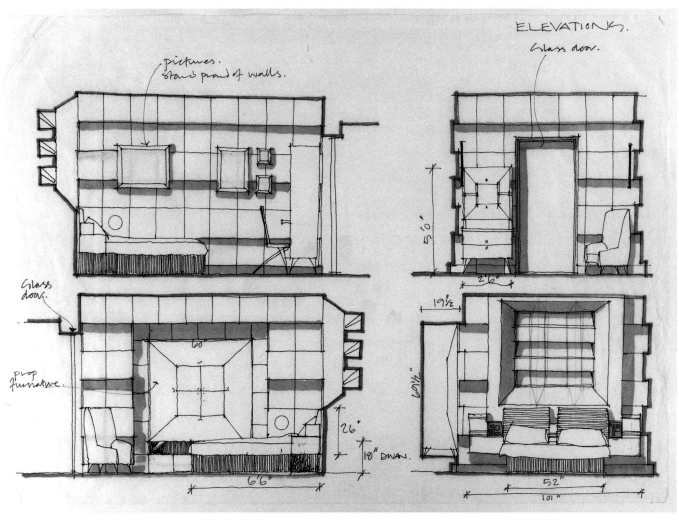

ELEVATIONS.
Glass door.

pictures.
Stand proud of walls.

Glass
door.

prop
furniture.

5'0"

2'6"

19½"

26"

18" DIVAN.

6'6"

52"

101"

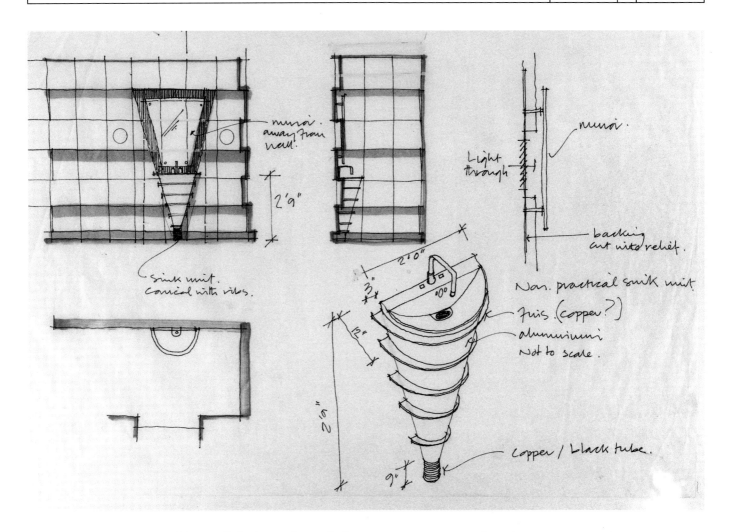

DREDD: "The same. Clones. Inhuman. Defective. He just broke down first."

HERSHEY: "No . . ."

DREDD: "You said I had no feelings, no emotions. Now you know why."

HERSHEY: "The Janus project didn't do that to you. You did that to yourself."

He turns, startled. Realizes she's right. Fergie enters.

FERGIE: "I'm sorry, guys. I can't fix this terminal out here."

DREDD: "We have to find Rico. We have to find Janus."

HERSHEY: "If the Janus project is back on line, they're gonna need a lot of power." (thinking) "Wait a second. Just before they blew up my Lawmaster in

Sector 4, there was a power surge at least three blocks wide. That's my beat, I know it well. The last time I felt something like that, the whole power grid in that area was shut down."

She's onto something. Dredd joins in . . .

DREDD: ". . . that the Statue of Liberty could be relocated on top of it. I know that sector well, too."

HERSHEY: "If there were an irregular signal in that area, we would be able to pick it up."

She looks at Dredd, pleased with herself. He smiles back.

HERSHEY: "I got a feeling about this, Dredd."

FERGIE: (interrupting) "So now that we've got that cleared up, I'd like to leave. The Judge Hunters are coming. You know, pain, death, mayhem."

DREDD: "Let's do it."

Opposite top: *Elevation of Hershey's apartment.*

Opposite bottom: *Elevations of the bedroom in Hershey's apartment.*

Above: *Bathroom plans in Hershey's apartment with an interesting sink design.*

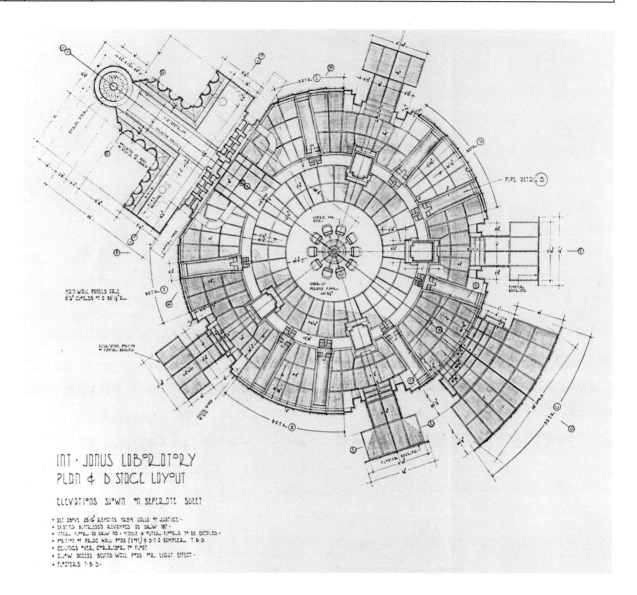

INT · JANUS LABORATORY
PLAN & D STAGE LAYOUT

ELEVATIONS SHOWN ON SEPARATE SHEET

· SET DRIVE 25'0" REMAINS FROM WALLS OF JUSTICE ·
· EXISTING BUTTRESSES REVAMPED AS SKEW 187 ·
· INNER FLOOR AS DRAW 70 · MIDDLE & OUTER FLOORS TO BE DETAILED ·
· PORTION OF PERIC WALL PODS (24FT) & D.N.A. SAMPLER. T.B.D
· CEILINGS OVER CORRIDORS TO FLOAT
· GLOW ACCESS BEHIND WALL PODS FOR LIGHT EFFECT ·
· FOOTERS T.B.D·

INT. DOOR TO JANUS LAB – NIGHT

Griffin enters, sees Rico and Ilsa. Crosses quickly towards them. We notice, but Griffin doesn't, that there is a whole new electricity between the two of them.

GRIFFIN: "Dredd got away from the Hunters."

RICO: "Don't worry. He's going to be seriously outnumbered. Right, Central?"

CENTRAL: "Correct, Council Judge Rico. The new DNA sample has been multi-plexed and the gametes are already dividing."

GRIFFIN: (stunned) "New sample? What the hell's going on?"

RICO: "Hey, that old DNA was in there for over thirty years. Sooner or later you gotta clean out the fridge."

GRIFFIN: (furious) "That sample was created from the finest specimens on the Council of Judges! What did you replace it with?"

Rico just smiles.

GRIFFIN: "My God. You didn't –?"

RICO: "Congratulate me. I'm going to be a father."

Rico walks away from him, past Ilsa, touching her arm. She smiles a wicked smile. Griffin looks at her, not understanding.

GRIFFIN: "Rico. You don't know what you're doing. The sample has to be pure of defects or the accelerators will form mutations. It's what happened

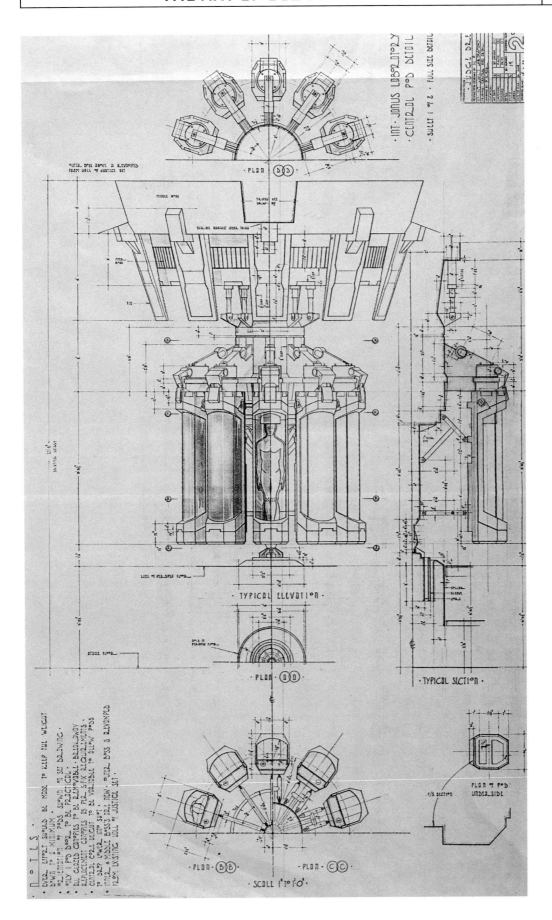

Left and opposite: *Elevations of
the Janus lab by Peter Russell.*

First concept of the doors to the Janus lab by Simon Murton.

before."

RICO: "That's why Dredd's so ugly."

GRIFFIN: "No, you, for God's sake, listen! You were defective. Your copies will be even more defective."

RICO: (tempered) "You're lying! All you care about is control. The Janus Judges won't be the puppets you want, they'll be my brothers and sisters, they'll follow me."

GRIFFIN: (voice hushed) "Sisters?"

RICO: "While I'm at it I'm going to breed some more. The old-fashioned way."

Griffin looks from Rico to Ilsa and back again, suddenly seeing clearly what he's created here.
  CLUNK! Behind him stands the ABC robot, its head and burning-red eyes craning down towards him with a growl.

GRIFFIN: (to Ilsa) "You . . . you're with him on

RICO: "I'm alive, Griffin, flesh and blood. Not one of your brainwashed machines you call Judges, but a real human."

GRIFFIN: (struggling) "Let me go! Central! Help me!"

CENTRAL: "I'm sorry, Chief Justice. The ABC robot is not tied into my main processor."

RICO: "That's right, Griff. You've gotta get into this high-tech stuff. Robot, tear off Judge Griffin's arms and legs. Save his head for last."

Griffin screams with fear. And then as Rico and Ilsa watch, and the horrible shadows appear on the wall, the screams become far, far worse.

Rico watches with wincing amusement, like a spectator at a rough hockey game. Ilsa watches with sick fascination.

RICO: (smiling) "Central, Chief Justice Griffin has retired. Therefore, I believe, in his absence, I must assume his responsibilities. Send in the clones."

EXT. RED QUAD, SECTION 5 – SOMEWHERE UP HIGH – NIGHT

The oldest part of the city, with buildings and architecture from our era and even earlier. The flying Lawmaster has just landed on a rubble-strewn surface. Hershey checks her Lawgiver.

Dredd thumbs shells into the Remington, then racks the slide one-handed like a Western hero.

FERGIE: "I'll stay here and watch the bike."

DREDD: (dragging him forward) "We might need you to shut down the Janus system."

FERGIE: "I knew you were gonna say that."

DREDD: (to Hershey) "Down there?"

HERSHEY: (checking scanner) "Down there."

They all shine their torches to illuminate a large spiral staircase.

INT. BUILDING – NIGHT

Dredd, Hershey and Fergie move down through the long-neglected building. Bats flutter past. Only Fergie ducks.

this . . .?"

ILSA: "You've never understood the full potential of this opportunity. This project needs vision, not politics."

Griffin draws his gun but it has barely cleared the holster when the robot grabs Griffin's wrist and plucks the weapon from his hand as if he's a child and hangs on to him.

The robot grabs Griffin with its other hand and lifts him off the ground.

*The first version of the Janus
lab anteroom with elevator,
drawn by Matt Codd.*

Above and opposite:
*Executive producer Andy
Vajna wanted an enormous
Janus lab with many pods.
These versions were drawn
by Julian Caldow.*

HERSHEY: "Power surge this way."

Before them are large steel doors.

HERSHEY: (puzzled) "No, wait, it moved . . . over
to . . ."

*From nowhere, as she turns to look around, the ABC
robot lunges out of the shadows and grabs her off
her feet. She drops her Lawgiver and scanner.*

HERSHEY: "Dredd!"

*The robot holds Hershey with one hand, opens fire
with the other. Fergie is hit. Dredd throws the
wounded hacker to relative safety, swings up the
ancient Remington, fires at the robot!*

HERSHEY: "Dredd!"

*She flinches even though she knows Dredd is aiming
around her. But Dredd's bullets barely dent the
robot. He moves forward.*

   Dredd and the ABC robot advance on each other

*like Hong Kong gunmen, blasting away. Dredd's
shots bounce off the robot's armor. At the same time,
some of the robot's shots miss Dredd, some bounce
off his armor, and one shot wings his shoulder. But
Dredd keeps on coming.*

   *A bullet hits the tendon-like control wire on the
robot's leg. The wire snaps. The robot goes down
with an electronic scream, but holds onto Hershey.*

   *A pneumatic door slides open suddenly. Rico and
Ilsa are there, backlit, both armed.*

RICO: "Enough, Dredd. Drop your gun."

DREDD: "No." (starting to aim) "Edsel here still
has another kneecap."

The robot looks sharply at Dredd.

RICO: "Amusing. Robot. On a count of three . . .
break Judge Hershey's neck. One . . . two . . ."

DREDD: "Hershey?"

HERSHEY: "I'm alright."

Dredd drops the Remington beside Hershey's Lawgiver.

RICO: "How human. You've become a romantic, brother."

Ilsa approaches the weapons. She picks up the Remington and starts to reach for the Lawgiver. Dredd and Hershey sneak a glance at each other. Suddenly Ilsa grins, laughs, and kicks the gun away.

RICO: "She's such a tease." (harsher) "Inside, now." (to robot) "If they move, crush them."

Dredd is taken away and the pneumatic door closes, leaving Hershey and Fergie in darkness with the robot.

INT. JANUS LAB

Dredd is marched in between Rico and Ilsa.

ILSA: "He looks like you."

RICO: "He is a lot like me."

DREDD: "I'm nothing like you."

RICO: "Wrong, the only difference between us is that you destroyed your life to embrace the law. I destroyed the law to embrace life. And speaking of life." (the insect-like clone pods descend) "Behold, the future."

Dredd watches the lab fully activate itself. Hundreds of clones are growing all around him.

RICO: "This is where we were born, brother! Can you feel it? You see, Joseph . . . "

Dredd stares at a mutant Rico as its moist eyes slowly open.

RICO: "You knew all along you were different."

INT. JANUS LAB – LANDING

The ABC robot stands guard, Hershey still in its metal grip. She struggles but can't free herself. Fergie groans and opens his eyes.

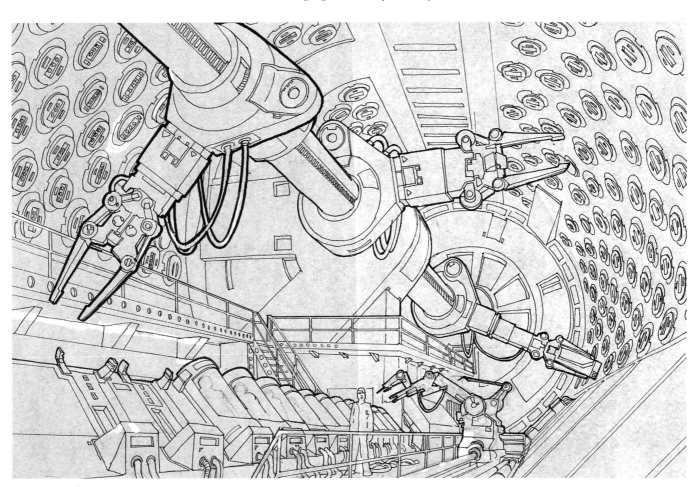

Above: *A table from the Janus lab by Julian Caldow.*

Left: *An early version of the central clone pods in the Janus lab, drawn by Simon Murton.*

HERSHEY: "Fergie, are you alive?"

FERGIE: "Unfortunately, yes."

He presses one hand against his wound, then sees Hershey's predicament. He looks at the robot from head to toe.

HERSHEY: "I don't like what you're thinking."

FERGIE: "Neither do I."

INT. JANUS LAB

RICO: "Look, Joseph. These are your brothers and your sisters, to be born in a few hours. An endless supply of perfection. Now we have a choice. To create a race of robots, like that thing out there, and call them Judges, or a race of free-thinking people and call them human."

DREDD: "You're diseased. You couldn't control yourself. What makes you think you can control them?"

Two versions of the central clone pods drawn by Julian Caldow.

RICO: "But you're in control. I'm appointing you

head of the new order. You choose."

DREDD: "You'll get nothing from me."

RICO: "That's what I've wondered all these years. Why? Why did you judge me?"

DREDD: "You killed innocent people."

RICO: ". . . a means to an end."

DREDD: "You caused a massacre."

RICO: "No. A revolution."

DREDD: "You betrayed the law."

RICO: "I was your blood, your brother. I'm the only family you ever had and you sent me to my death and you talk about betrayal. We were the ones who were innocent, your Council's failed experiment. Do you want to do to them what they did to you? When are you gonna stop being a slave and grow up? Now choose."

DREDD: "Rico?"

RICO: "Joseph?"

DREDD: (long pause) "You're gonna have to kill me."

RICO: "Why?"

DREDD: "It's your only hope."

RICO: "Fido! Tear that bitch's arms and legs off."

DREDD: "Don't do it!"

RICO: "You're right, it's no way to treat a lady." (to the robot) "Rip his arms and legs off. Slowly."

The robot turns, clanks, moves between Rico and Ilsa. It then turns, drops Hershey – and backhands Rico!

Rico flips over backwards, drops down a level! Ilsa runs forward – and the robot knocks her aside, too!

Dredd is astonished – until he sees Fergie, hanging on the back of the robot, his hands deep inside it working the circuits.

FERGIE: "Yee-HAH!"

HERSHEY: "Dredd! Catch!"

She throws him the Remington that Ilsa dropped. Dredd spins and fires down at Rico, who dives for cover as he grabs his Lawgiver and fires back up at Dredd.

Ilsa jumps to her feet, right into Hershey's fist! Fergie hangs onto the robot as it staggers around, trying to regain control of its own movements. Fergie sees it's reaching for him and reaches into the body cavity as far as he can. He throws a switch and the robot's head goes into a spasm of electrical chaos. Fergie is thrown off and hits the floor hard. Something inside him breaks. But he still has enough strength to look up.

FERGIE: "Hack you . . . asshole."

Smoke billows from the robot's head. Slowly, it topples. CRASH! Fergie slumps down and lies still.

Ilsa and Hershey continue to struggle hand to

hand. Ilsa breaks free and goes into whirling Karate moves, finishing with a savage kick to Hershey's crotch. Hershey grins.

HERSHEY: "You don't fight girls much, do you?"

She grabs Ilsa's ankle and flips her over backward.
Dredd sees Fergie in the doorway and crawls over to him. Fergie's ashen, his shirt soaked with blood.

DREDD: "Fergie!"

FERGIE: (weakly) "Say it, Dredd."

A puzzled pause. Then Dredd remembers.

DREDD: "I . . . I made a mistake . . . I . . . I'm sorry I misjudged you."

FERGIE: "And you'll never arrest me again."

DREDD: "And I'll never arrest you again."

FERGIE: "Damn straight."

DREDD: "Take it easy, friend."

FERGIE: (he's going) "Dredd . . . get him."

He dies. Dredd closes his eyes. His face fills with fury. With a violent gesture, he cocks the shotgun.

DREDD: "RICOOOOOO!"

He whirls and charges into the open, marching forward like a one-man mobile artillery charge.
In the lab it's like a fireworks display as round after round smashes into the high-tech machinery, sparks everywhere. Mind totally blown, Rico tries to aim, but then the bullets start to seek him out! He turns and runs! The glorious lab starts to shake and shudder. The place is gonna blow.
Rico dives behind some consoles. Armor-piercing rounds chase him, punching holes just above his head. Equipment sparks and smokes. Rico takes cover, lowers his voice.

RICO: "Central! Hatch the first set of clones, now!"

CENTRAL: "The cloning process is not finished, Chief Justice Rico. Clones will be only 60 per cent complete."

RICO: "I need reinforcements! Hatch the goddamn clones, now!"

CENTRAL: "Beginning hatching process . . . now."

A version of the clone pod drawn by Julian Caldow, but considered too expensive to develop.

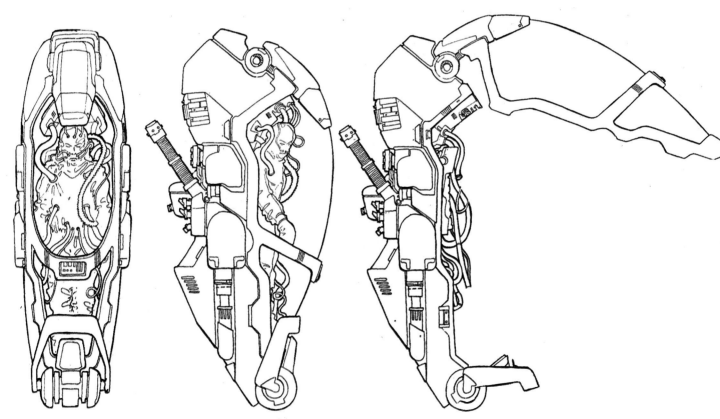

(after a pause, quietly) "I know we're going to regret this."

The lab sparks and crackles. All around the lab, the incubators start to slide out from the walls.

Nearby, Hershey and Ilsa are grappling. They roll into the workshop area. Hershey gets a choke hold on her. Ilsa grabs a wrench, smashes it over Hershey's head. Hershey falls. Ilsa turns and kicks Hershey viciously. Hershey lands face first on an incubator – and the clone inside wakes up! Its eyes burn into Hershey's. The incubator creaks open. A clone is oozing out right in front of her. It's half formed, raw muscle and sinew barely covering its bones.

In shock, Ilsa backs away, drops the wrench. The clumsy clone stumbles and falls. Hershey recoils in shock, as does Ilsa. The weak clone collapses. Hershey grits her teeth, her anger swelling. WHACK! She punches Ilsa as hard as she can. The fight continues.

Dredd fumbles along in the smoke. He is suddenly grabbed, and turns, expecting Rico, but it is another half-formed clone. It mews horribly and clutches at him. Dredd stares at it, appalled by its very existence. They look into each other's eyes, which are eerily the same. The clone is weak, distressed.

CLONE: "P . . . Pain. Pain."

Dredd grits his teeth and votes pro-choice. BLAM! The clone falls away, vanishing in the smoke. CLICK, CLICK. Dredd's out of ammo.

Hershey and Ilsa are still fighting. Ilsa gets in one, two, three terrific blows.

ILSA: "Bitch!"

HERSHEY: "Judge Bitch!"

Hershey clobbers her with a right!

On the lower level, Rico prowls through the smoke, looking for Dredd, his Lawgiver ammo light blinking. The lab is shaking, sparks are raining all over.

Rico spies the exit and head for it. From nowhere, Dredd dives on Rico! Each man grabs the other's wrists. Rico's weapon fires wildly, inches from Dredd's face. The brothers carom off sparking equipment. Incubators smash around them, their doors opening.

A short stairwell breaks their fall. The Lawgiver falls beside Rico, who reaches for it. Dredd tries to stop him. Rico is stronger. He grips the gun.

RICO: "GRENADE!"

GUN VOICE: "All lethal rounds exhausted. Select."

RICO: "STANDARD BULLET!"

VOICE: "All lethal rounds exhausted. Select."

RICO: "SMOKE BOMB!"

BAM! The round hits Dredd like a pile driver. His shirt catches fire. He falls backwards over a railing as smoke coils upwards.

RICO: "Central! Turn off overhead lighting!"

The main lights go out. Only the floor lights remain. Rico grins, runs out. In the central dais of the lab, sparks fly and machinery rumbles.

Ilsa and Hershey are surprised by the sudden darkness. Ilsa falls, sliding on the slick floor. Hershey, limping, comes towards her. Ilsa foot-sweeps her to the floor.

On the floor below, chest blackened, trying to catch his breath, Dredd reacts as the lights go out. Seeing a light in the smoke, he crawls toward it. Then his face falls. The light is one of Central's eyes.

DREDD: "Central! Can you –"

CENTRAL: "You are an escaped convict, Dredd. I advise you to surrender."

DREDD: "Okay, you win. I'll give myself up to Chief Justice Rico. Where is he?"

CENTRAL: (helpful) "Oh, he went upstairs." (turning on lights) "Straight ahead to your right."

Dredd looks over at the still peaceful body of Fergie. Sparks cascade over him. There is a rumble. KABOOM! The central dais is toast.

DREDD: "Thank you."

Dredd goes for the door. One more look at Fergie as the lab goes up all around him. Then Dredd dives out.

Elsewhere, Hershey is thrown backwards. BAM! The incubators' machinery blows up. The lab is history.

EXT. STRUCTURE HEAD

Rico is starting the Lawmaster Mark IV.

DREDD'S VOICE: "RICO!"

Opposite and previous page: Two views of the Statue of Liberty. The painting on the previous page was used in Matt Codd's storyboard for an early version of the ending.

Rico turns – too late. Dredd tackles him out of the saddle! The bike crashes out of the opening. As it drops to street level, Rico and Dredd continue to fight – in the head of the Statue of Liberty!

They trade punches high above the city. It is raining now, violent lightning strobes the statue. The Lawgiver skids out of reach. For a moment, Dredd has the advantage. Then Rico connects with Dredd's chest wound. Dredd almost folds. Rico is almost as tired as Dredd, but Dredd is in agony.

RICO: "This is how you repay me for telling the truth?"

Rico hits Dredd on the wound again.

RICO: "I'm the only one who never lied to you, brother."

Dredd falls, rolls to the edge of the precipice! Rico grins, struggles to full height.

RICO: (catching his breath) "Joseph Dredd. I hereby judge you. To the charge of betraying you best friend . . . GUILTY. To the charge of betraying you own flesh . . . GUILTY."

Rico leans over the helpless Dredd, kicks him viciously. Dredd slips over the edge, dangles over the chasm!

RICO: "And finally . . . to the charge of being human when we could have been gods . . . GUILTY."

Rico picks up the Lawgiver. Puts it right against Dredd's head.

RICO: "The sentence is DEATH!"

Right: *Left side elevation showing the hole in the head of the Statue of Liberty, drawn by Martin Laing.*

Opposite: *Plan and elevations of the interior and exterior of the Statue of Liberty head, drawn by Don Dossett.*

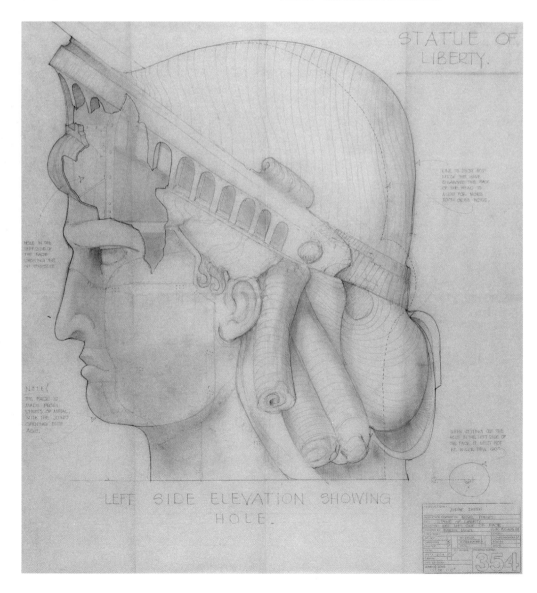

SOFT GUN VOICE: "All lethal rounds exhausted. Select."

Dredd dares everything. He grabs Rico's hand! Dredd's finger makes contact with the pistol grip. A beep of recognition.

GUN VOICE: "DNA accepted. Select."

DREDD: "Signal flare!"

Dredd uses his last remaining strength to force the gun upward. The signal flare goes off like a rocket. Rico is blinded. He loses his balance and tumbles from the statue. At the last instant Dredd grabs Rico's hand, using all his strength to pull them both up.

Rico smiles, fearless, into Dredd's eyes.

RICO: "You saved me, Joe?"

Dredd doesn't understand his brother's calm.

DREDD: "You don't have to die."

RICO: (eyes light up) "I won't."

Rico brings up his other hand and forces Dredd's grip away.

RICO: "Life, Joseph, life."

DREDD: "No."

The last finger is forced away as Rico drops, his eyes fixed on his brother as he plummets downward.

Dredd has lost his only brother. He has no

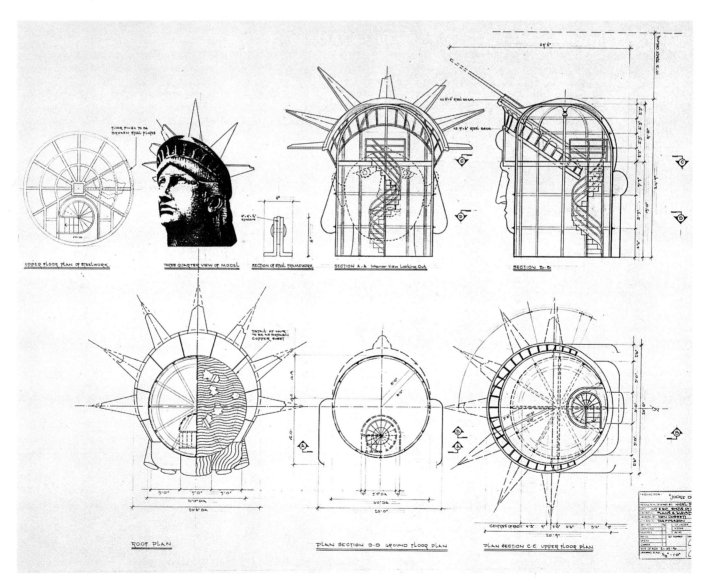

strength left. His face and body are bleeding. He starts to climb back up.

Suddenly, a boot steps on his hand! He looks up and sees Ilsa, bruised, bloody, and angry! She holds out the shotgun, with her finger on the trigger. And then . . .

BLAM! Ilsa falls dead, shot in the back. Hershey appears, her gun smoking, reaches down for Dredd's hand, pulls him up.

EXT. BASE OF THE STATUE OF LIBERTY – DAWN

Dredd exits the building, with Hershey behind him. They both look like shit. In front of them, what looks like the entire Mega-City police force fills the street.

Dredd looks at all their faces: young cadets, Judges, Judge Hunters. They watch the hero in silent awe. Then a chant begins.

THE CROWD: "Judge DREDD! Judge DREDD! Judge DREDD!"

Golden light cuts across the steps as the sunrise breaks through the clouds. The imposing Chief Judge Hunter starts to move forward. Flanked by two other Hunters. They ominously approach Dredd. The crowd splits, sensing a showdown. The chanting dies completely as the Judge Hunter raises his arms.

DREDD: (to Hershey) "Stand back."

The Chief Judge Hunter arrives in front of Dredd.

DREDD: "Am I under arrest?"

There is a tense moment of silence.

JUDGE HUNTER: "That won't be necessary."

The two warriors stare at each other with mutual respect. Olmeyer fights his way through the crowd.

OLMEYER: "Central broadcast the Janus plans after Griffin's death."

JUDGE HUNTER: "We owe you a debt of gratitude."

The crowd roars its approval. The Chief Hunter hands Dredd his helmet, another brings forth his armor.

DREDD: "Thank you."

He glances at Hershey, who smiles.

JUDGE HUNTER: (over the crowd) "We have to reconstitute the Council, Judge Dredd. We'd like you to consider the first position of Chief Justice."

DREDD: "I'm a Street Judge." (motions to Hershey, who steps forward) "I recommend Judge Hershey."

JUDGE HUNTER: "Hershey, would you consider it?"

She doesn't know what to say. Dredd starts to move to a waiting Lawmaster cycle.

DREDD: "Don't be dumb. It's a good career move."

Dredd straddles his bike and fastens his shoulder armor. Hershey leaves the others behind to follow Dredd.

HERSHEY: "Let me think about it."

HERSHEY: "That's it? A near-death experience and no good-bye?"

DREDD: "Good-bye, Hershey."

Dread puts his helmet on. Reflected in the visor are the other Judges and police lights.

HERSHEY: "Welcome back, Judge Dredd."

Hershey kisses him.

DREDD: "Code 212. Illegal Physical Contact with a Judge."

HERSHEY: (whispers) "Bullshit. Feels good to be human, doesn't it?"

DREDD: "I knew you'd say that."

Dredd smiles for the first time and starts the bike, roaring off as the crowd cheers. The bike rolls away as the cheering fades in the distance . . .

Dissolving to a night shot of Dredd high atop the City Hall. Astride his Lawmaster he surveys the city lights below. He puts on his helmet with a sense of purpose and starts the engine. The Lawman soars into the night, swooping down into the chaos of the city he loves until he becomes just another light in the vista of Mega-City.

FADE OUT

THE END

Joseph Dredd,
greatest
Street Judge
of them all.
Painting by
Kevin Walker.